INTERVAL ANALYSIS

Prentice-Hall
Series in Automatic Computation

George Forsythe, editor

BAUMANN, FELICIANO, BAUER, AND SAMELSON, *Introduction to Algol*
CESCHINO AND KUNTZMANN, *Numerical Solution of Initial Value Problems*
DESMONDE, *Computers and Their Uses*
DESMONDE, *Real-Time Data Processing Systems: Introductory Concepts*
GOLDEN, *FORTRAN IV: Programming and Computing*
HARTMANIS AND STEARNS, *Algebraic Structure Theory of Sequential Machines*
HULL, *Introduction to Computing*
MARTIN, *Systems Analysis for Real-Time Computers*
MARTIN, *Programming Real-Time Computer Systems*
MINSKY, *Computation: Finite and Infinite Machines*
MOORE, *Interval Analysis*
SCHULTZ, *Digital Processing: A System Orientation*
SNYDER, *Chebyshev Methods in Numerical Approximation*
STROUD AND SECREST, *Gaussian Quadrature Formulas*
TRAUB, *Iterative Methods for the Solution of Equations*
VARGA, *Matrix Iterative Analysis*
WILKINSON, *Rounding Errors in Algebraic Processes*

PRENTICE-HALL INTERNATIONAL, INC., *London*
PRENTICE-HALL OF AUSTRALIA, PTY. LTD., *Sydney*
PRENTICE-HALL OF CANADA, LTD., *Toronto*
PRENTICE-HALL OF INDIA (PRIVATE), LTD., *New Delhi*
PRENTICE-HALL OF JAPAN, INC., *Tokyo*

INTERVAL ANALYSIS

RAMON E. MOORE
Associate Professor of Computer Sciences
University of Wisconsin

PRENTICE-HALL, INC.

ENGLEWOOD CLIFFS, N. J.

Library of Congress Catalog Card No. 66-22090

Printed in the United States of America
47685-C

to Judy

PREFACE

This book is addressed to the mathematician, the numerical analyst, and the programmer.

The title refers to a set of concepts and techniques based on treating an *interval* of real numbers as a new kind of number, represented by a pair of real numbers, namely, its left and right endpoints.

The techniques can be programmed for computers in order to obtain simultaneously upper and lower bounds to exact solutions of equations of various types.

Many stored-program digital computers are now big enough and fast enough that it has become feasible to mechanize parts of numerical analysis. For example, direct use can be made of truncated Taylor series expansions, with remainder bounded by the computer. A practical method for the machine generation of Taylor coefficients is given in Chapter 11.

Computer programs can be written which will produce results of guaranteed accuracy in a single run on the computer with all the necessary analysis done by the computer during the course of a computation.

The application to systems of nonlinear ordinary differential equations is carried out in considerable detail. Examples of results obtained on the computer help to show the extent to which the methods are already of practical value (Chapter 12).

The mathematician, the numerical analyst, and the programmer will find a number of interesting and challenging research problems concerned with ways in which the methods and programs can be extended, refined, and improved.

The material in this book was presented as a graduate course in the Computer Sciences Department of the University of Wisconsin during the summer of 1965. A number of exercises have been included to aid the reader in understanding the methods by giving him practice on simple but illustrative applications. Some programming problems are also included.

Much of the research was done while the author was a member of the Applied Mathematics Department of the Lockheed Missiles and Space Company in Palo Alto, California. Some of the results have been reported in the Lockheed technical reports referenced in the text. Some of the results appeared in the author's dissertation at Stanford University. Two lectures were given on the work at seminars held by the Mathematics Research Center, United States Army, at the University of Wisconsin in October 1964 and April 1965. The proceedings of those seminars have appeared in book form in the two volumes of *Error in Digital Computation* referenced in the text. Part of the work and the actual writing of the book was done while the author was a visiting member of the Mathematics Research Center. A brief summary of the methods was given at the IFIP Congress, 1965.

The author is fortunate to have received encouragement and helpful suggestions from many quarters, but especially from George Forsythe, Ray Boche, Eldon Hansen, Allen Reiter, Wayman Strother, and C. T. Yang. The present work exists largely as the result of an interplay between ideas and machine computations made possible by the outstanding computer programming of R. E. Boche, J. A. Davison, M. Halpern, H. R. Jaschke, A. Reiter, S. Shayer, and many others. Thanks go to Miss Melba Marty for typing the manuscript.

RAMON E. MOORE

CONTENTS

12 NUMERICAL RESULTS WITH THE Kth-ORDER METHOD 119

13 COORDINATE TRANSFORMATIONS FOR THE INITIAL-VALUE PROBLEM 131

APPENDICES 141

INDEX 143

INTERVAL ANALYSIS

1 INTRODUCTION

1.1 THE METHOD OF ARCHIMEDES

A very old example of a "two-sided approximation" is afforded by a method due to Archimedes. He considered the circle and devised a method for finding the ratio of the circumference to the diameter. What is of special interest here is the kind of answer he obtained. He considered inscribed polygons and circumscribing polygons and obtained an increasing sequence of lower bounds and at the same time a decreasing sequence of upper bounds. Thus, stopping the process with a circumscribing and an inscribed polygon each of n sides, he obtained, in effect, an interval containing the desired result, namely, the number π. By choosing n large enough, an interval of arbitrarily small width can be found in this way containing the number π.

PROBLEM 1.1. Using the method of Archimedes, find some intervals containing π. For example, use a pair of squares and a pair of hexagons.

1.2 SIGNIFICANT FIGURES

The decimal representation of real numbers affords a means of writing an approximation of arbitrarily high precision to a real number by putting down enough "significant figures"—that is, by writing sufficiently many digits in the decimal expansion. In fact, by writing down no more decimal digits than are known to be correct in the decimal expansion of a real number, we obtain an approximate value whose precision is exhibited by the number of figures written down and whose error cannot be more than one in the last decimal place written. Of course, by rounding the last figure in the usual way we can reduce this maximum error by a factor of one-half.

The rules for performing arithmetic operations with decimal numbers are simple and universally known. The process of "long division," for example, amounts to a *digit-by-digit* determination of a quotient of two decimal numbers. A few digit-by-digit methods for other than purely arithmetic operations can be constructed fairly easily—for example, for the square root of a decimal number and for the conversion of decimal expansions to binary expansions. A digit-by-digit method has the advantage of a precise indication of accuracy at each step. On the other hand, for most types of involved problems there are no reasonably direct digit-by-digit methods available.

Most practical problems requiring extensive numerical computation involve *quantities determined experimentally by approximate measurements*— very often with some estimate of the accuracy of the measured values. A typical calculation will begin with some numbers known only to a certain number of significant decimal digits. Results computed from such *inexact initial data* will also be of limited precision. It is of great practical importance to be able to assess the accuracy of such results. A number of analytical techniques are available for estimating the sensitivity of final results with respect to small changes in initial data.

Many of those amount to assuming linear dependence and involve estimating the derivative of a result with respect to an initial variable. In practice computational problems of such complexity arise that the application of these analytical methods is often too laborious for human execution in a reasonable interval of time. As an alternative, a common practice is to repeat a machine computation with several sets of nearby initial values—sometimes a very large number, if there are very many inexact initial quantities affecting the final results.

In fairly short computations a few rules of thumb for keeping track of significant figures are usually adequate. On the other hand when the number of arithmetic operations between the initial data and the results reaches the tens of millions, these rules of thumb can give totally misleading estimates of accuracy. Many modern digital computers perform on the order of a million arithmetic operations a second. Problems can and do find their way onto these machines requiring many hours for completion.

We will give an example now of a computation involving only a very small number of arithmetic operations that already foils a scheme sometimes thought to be adequate for an estimation of rounding error. The idea is to perform the same computation twice, carrying a greater number of significant figures in the arithmetic the second time. The number of figures to which the two sets of results agree is supposed to be the actual number of correct figures in the first set of results.

A shortcoming of this scheme is shown by the following example.

Consider the recursion formula

$$x_{n+1} = x_n^2 \tag{1-1}$$

and suppose that $x_0 = 1 - 10^{-21}$. We wish to compute x_{75}.

If we perform the computation using ten-place decimal arithmetic, we obtain the approximate values

$$x_0 = 1, \quad x_1 = 1, \quad \ldots, \quad x_{75} = 1$$

If we perform the computation using twenty-place decimal arithmetic, we obtain the same approximate values, so the two values for x_{75} in particular agree to all ten places carried in the first computation. However, the exact value is

$$x_{75} = (1 - 10^{-21})^{2^{75}} < (1 - 10^{-21})^{10^{22.5}}$$

or

$$x_{75} < \{(1 - 10^{-21})^{10^{21}}\}^{31.6} < e^{-31.6} < 10^{-10}$$

PROBLEM 1.2. Verify the above inequalities.

On the basis of this example, or should we say "counterexample," it is evident that repeating a calculation with more significant figures does not necessarily provide a basis for the determination of the number of significant figures in the results. Of course, it *is* true that by carrying *enough* places a result of arbitrarily high precision can be found in any computation involving only a finite number of real arithmetic operations beginning with exactly known real numbers. Unfortunately, it is often prohibitively difficult to tell in advance of a computation how many places must be carried in order to guarantee results of required precision.

If, instead of simply computing a numerical approximation using limited-precision arithmetic and then worrying later about the precision of the results, we proceed in the spirit of the method of Archimedes to construct intervals known in advance to contain the desired exact result, then our main concerns will be the narrowness of the intervals we obtain and the amount of computation required to get them.

The methods we are going to discuss in the subsequent chapters will yield for the example above, for instance, an interval close to [0, 1] using only ten-decimal-place "interval arithmetic," but the methods will yield an interval of arbitrarily small width containing the exact result by carrying enough places; in this case, obviously, more than twenty places are needed, in order to avoid getting 1 for the value of x_0.

REFERENCES

1. GORN, S., "The automatic analysis and control of computing errors," *J. Soc. Indust. Appl. Math.*, **2** (1954).
2. HOUSEHOLDER, A. S., *Principles of Numerical Analysis.* New York: McGraw-Hill Book Company, 1953.

2 INTERVAL NUMBERS

If we have, in addition to the results of a computation, error bounds for the differences between the results and the exact solution values, then no matter how these error bounds were obtained, whether by analytical means with pencil and paper prior to the computation or by further machine computations during or after the given computation or whatever, it will always be the case that we have, in effect, for each exact result sought, a *pair* of numbers: an approximate value and an error bound, or *an upper and a lower bound to the exact result.*

Extensions of number systems involving ordered pairs of numbers from the given system are commonplace. The rational numbers are essentially ordered pairs of integers; complex numbers are ordered pairs of real numbers; in each case arithmetic operations are defined with rules for computing the components of a pair resulting from an arithmetic operation on a *pair* of pairs. Pairs of special form are equivalent to numbers of the original type.

We define an *interval number* to be an ordered pair of real numbers, $[a, b]$, with $a \leq b$. Degenerate intervals of the form $[a, a]$ are equivalent to real numbers. In the next chapter we will discuss arithmetic operations on interval numbers.

An interval number is also a *set* of real numbers. The interval number $[a, b]$ is the set of real numbers x such that $a \leq x \leq b$.

Using the notation $\{x \mid P(x)\}$ for "the set of x such that the proposition $P(x)$ holds," we can write

$$[a, b] = \{x \mid a \leq x \leq b\}$$

We will frequently use the symbols $\in$, $\subset$, $\cup$, $\cap$, in the usual senses

5

of set theory. Thus $x \in [a, b]$ means x is a real number in the interval $a \leq x \leq b$. By $[a, b] \subset [c, d]$ we mean, of course, that the interval $[a, b]$ is contained as a set in the interval $[c, d]$, but not necessarily properly ; in other words, by $[a, b] \subset [c, d]$ we mean

$$c \leq a \leq b \leq d.$$

We use the notation $\cup$, $\cap$ for set union and intersection, respectively, in the usual senses.

From the inequalities

$$a \leq x \leq b, \qquad c \leq y \leq d \tag{2-1}$$

we can only conclude that

$$a + c \leq x + y \leq b + d \tag{2-2}$$

as far as bounds on $x + y$ are concerned.

PROBLEM 2.1. Prove that the inequalities (2-1) imply the inequalities (2-2) and that the inequalities (2-2) are sharp—that is, that they are attained.

If we had in the computer the number pairs $[a, b]$ and $[c, d]$ (say, storing a and b in successive cells, and c and d in successive memory cells), then the machine could, using ordinary "single-precision" arithmetic, compute not $a + c$ and $b + d$ but, rather, only approximate values to these sums. In other words, the machine-computed values for $a + c$ and $b + d$ are only accurate to the precision of the machine arithmetic used, even if a, b, c, and d are themselves exact.

For a given computing machine and a given set of arithmetic instructions in the operation code of that machine—for example, single-precision, normalized-floating-point unrounded arithmetic—it is possible to program the computation of the machine number closest to $a + c$ from below and the machine number closest to $b + d$ from above. (We will return to this point in the next chapter.) It is a matter of rounding the right endpoint, $b + d$, up and the left endpoint, $a + c$, down. No rounding is necessary, of course, when the machine result is known already to be on the appropriate side of the endpoint in question.

PROBLEM 2.2. Choosing a particular machine-number representation (e.g., normalized floating point, 36-bit mantissa) and a particular (corresponding) machine addition (e.g., normalized, unrounded), describe, in detail, a general scheme for obtaining the greatest machine-number lower bound for $a + c$ and the least machine-number upper bound for $b + d$.

We introduce now some further notation which will be used subsequently.

We denote the set of closed real intervals by $\mathscr{I}$. Thus, if $I \in \mathscr{I}$, then $I = [a, b]$ for some real numbers a and b such that $a \leq b$.
We denote the width of an interval $[a, b]$ by

$$w([a, b]) = b - a$$

We denote the "magnitude" of an interval by

$$|[a, b]| = \max(|a|, |b|)$$

We define a partial ordering of the elements of $\mathscr{I}$ by

$$[a, b] < [c, d] \qquad \text{if and only if } b < c$$

By $[a, b] = [c, d]$ we mean, of course, that $a = c$ and $b = d$.

PROBLEM 2.3. Represent the elements of $\mathscr{I}$, i.e., interval numbers, as points in the plane with left endpoints as abscissas and right endpoints as ordinates. Interpret geometrically the relation between the point representing an interval and the real numbers contained in the interval.

PROBLEM 2.4. Using the same representation as above, what is the locus of intervals of a given width ? What is the locus of the set of intervals containing a given real number ? Describe a graphical procedure for finding the union of two intersecting intervals.

3 INTERVAL ARITHMETIC

3.1 EXACT-INTERVAL ARITHMETIC

In this section we will introduce and discuss an arithmetic for the elements of $\mathscr{I}$, i. e., interval numbers, or more simply, intervals. The arithmetic will be an extension of real arithmetic, and we will assume in this section that endpoints are computed with infinite precision. In the next section we will discuss a modification to account for round-off error in machine-computed endpoints.

If $*$ is one of the symbols $+$, $-$, $\cdot$, $/$, we define arithmetic operations on intervals by

$$[a, b] * [c, d] = \{x * y \mid a \leq x \leq b, c \leq y \leq d\} \tag{3-1}$$

except that we do not define $[a, b] / [c, d]$ if $0 \in [c, d]$.

PROBLEM 3.1. Prove that the set of intervals is closed with respect to the arithmetic operations defined by equation (3-1), i. e., that the result is again an interval.

The definition of the interval arithmetic operations given by equation (3-1) is set-theoretic and emphasizes the fact that the sum, difference, product, or quotient of two intervals is just the set of sums, differences, products, or quotients, respectively, of pairs of real numbers, one from each of the two intervals.

An equivalent set of definitions of algebraic character in terms of formulas for the endpoints of resultant intervals is the following:

$$[a, b] + [c, d] = [a + c, b + d]$$

8

$$[a, b] - [c, d] = [a - d, b - c] \qquad (3\text{-}2)$$

$$[a, b] \cdot [c, d] = [\min(ac, ad, bc, bd), \max(ac, ad, bc, bd)]$$

and, if $0 \notin [c, d]$, then

$$[a, b] / [c, d] = [a, b] \cdot [1/d, 1/c]$$

PROBLEM 3.2. By testing the signs of the endpoints a, b, c, and d, break the formula for interval multiplication into nine cases only one of which requires more than two multiplications.

Henceforth we identify degenerate intervals of the form $[a, a]$ with the real numbers. From the definition given by equation (3-1) it is clear that with this identification interval arithmetic with degenerate intervals reduces to ordinary real arithmetic. Thus interval arithmetic is a generalization or an extension of real arithmetic.

It follows directly from the definition (3-1) that interval addition and interval multiplication are both associative and commutative; i. e., if I, J, and K are intervals, then the following equations hold:

$$I + (J + K) = (I + J) + K$$

$$I \cdot (J \cdot K) = (I \cdot J) \cdot K \qquad (3\text{-}3)$$

$$I + J = J + I$$

$$I \cdot J = J \cdot I$$

PROBLEM 3.3. Carry out the following exercises in interval arithmetic:

a. $[0, 1] + [1, 2] =$ e. $[-1, 1] / [-2, -1/2] =$

b. $[3, 3.1] - [0, 0.1] =$ f. $[-3, 2] \cdot [-3.1, 2.1] =$

c. $[-4, -1] \cdot [-6, 5] =$ g. $[1, 2] - [1, 2] =$

d. $2 \cdot [-1, 2] =$

The real numbers 0 and 1 are identities for interval addition and interval multiplication, respectively. In other words, for any interval I, we have

$$0 + I = I + 0 = I$$

and

$$1 \cdot I = I \cdot 1 = I$$

For convenience, we will often drop the dot indicating interval multiplication and use the simpler notation

$$IJ \equiv I \cdot J$$

The distributive law does *not* always hold for interval arithmetic. For example,

$$[1, 2]([1, 2] - [1, 2]) = [1, 2]([-1, 1]) = [-2, 2]$$

whereas

$$[1, 2][1, 2] - [1, 2][1, 2] = [1, 4] - [1, 4] = [-3, 3]$$

The failure of the distributive law is rare among algebraic systems in mathematics. Thus, as an abstract mathematical system, interval arithmetic is a very little studied subject.*

Making use of the fact that an interval is also a set (of real numbers), we do have the following important relation connecting interval addition and interval multiplication: for any intervals I, J, and K

$$I \cdot (J + K) \subset I \cdot J + I \cdot K \qquad (3-4)$$

We refer to the property of interval arithmetic expressed by equation (3–4) as *subdistributivity*.

PROBLEM 3.4. Prove the subdistributivity property (3–4) for interval arithmetic.

Some special cases in which distributivity does hold are useful. If t is real, then

$$t(I + J) = tI + tJ$$

If J and K contain only real numbers of the same sign so that $JK > 0$, then the inclusion in equation (3–4) can be replaced by equality.

PROBLEM 3.5. Show that $JK > 0$ implies $I(J + K) = IJ + IK$.

Additive and multiplicative inverses exist only for degenerate intervals, i. e., real numbers. One way to see this immediately is to notice that from the equation (3–1) defining interval arithmetic operations it is clear that if either operand contains two distinct real numbers then the resulting interval must contain at least two distinct real numbers and so cannot be equal to the degenerate interval containing only the single real number zero.

Interval arithmetic is *inclusion monotonic*, that is to say, if $I \subset K$, and $J \subset L$, then

$$I + J \subset K + L$$
$$I - J \subset K - L$$
$$IJ \subset KL \qquad (3-5)$$
$$I/J \subset K/L \qquad (\text{if } 0 \notin L)$$

This set of relations follows immediately from the definition (3–1). From the transitivity of the inclusion relation ($I \subset J$ *and* $J \subset K$ implies $I \subset K$) and the set of relations (3–5) we arrive at the following important result.

---

*See, however, R.C. Young, "The algebra of many-valued quantities," *Math. Annalen*, **104** (1931), 260–290.

THEOREM 3.1. If $F(X_1, X_2, \ldots, X_n)$ is a *rational* expression in the interval variables $X_1, X_2, \ldots, X_n$, i. e., a finite combination of $X_1, \ldots, X_n$ and a finite set of constant intervals with interval arithmetic operations, then

$$X'_1 \subset X_1, \ldots, X'_n \subset X_n \quad \text{implies} \quad F(X'_1, \ldots, X'_n) \subset F(X_1, \ldots, X_n)$$

for every set of interval numbers $X_1, \ldots, X_n$ for which the interval arithmetic operations in F are defined.

Notice from the relations (3–5) that if $0 \notin L$ and $J \subset L$, then $0 \notin J$, and if K/L is defined, then so is K/J.

In the special case that $X'_1, \ldots, X'_n$ and the constant intervals in the expression F are real numbers, the value of $F(X'_1, \ldots, X'_n)$ will be a real number contained in the interval $F(X_1, \ldots, X_n)$. In this way, by evaluating a finite number of interval arithmetic operations we can bound the range of values of a real rational function over intervals of values for each of its arguments.

If $f(x_1, x_2, \ldots, x_n)$ is real rational expression in which each variable x_i occurs only once, i. e., appears only once and only to the first power ($x_1^2 = x_1 \cdot x_1$ is taken as *two* occurrences), then the corresponding interval expression $F(X_1, \ldots, X_n)$ will compute the actual range of values of f for $x_i \in X_i$; in this case,

$$F(X_1, \ldots, X_n) = \{f(x_1, x_2, \ldots, x_n) \mid x_i \in X_i, i = 1, 2, \ldots, n\}.$$

This follows from (3–1) by a set-theoretic argument. In effect, each x_i ranges independently over the corresponding interval X_i.

PROBLEM 3.6. Using interval arithmetic, compute bounds on the ranges of values of the following real rational functions over the indicated domains:
a. $f(x) = x(1 - x), 0 \le x \le 1$.
b. $f(x, y) = xy, -1 \le x \le 1, -1 \le y \le 1$.
c. $f(x) = x/(1 + x), 0 \le x \le 1$.
d. $f(x) = x^7 + x^3 - .6x^2 + .11x - .006, 0 \le x \le .2$.

3.2 ROUNDED-INTERVAL ARITHMETIC

So-called "single-precision" arithmetic operations on a fixed-word-length digital computer, whether fixed- or floating point arithmetic is involved, usually provide access to the remainder in one form of another in order to permit the determination of results of arbitrarily high precision through the programming of multiple-precision routines. Thus, for example, the exact product of two machine numbers each consisting of s binary digits can have as many as $2s$ dinary digits in its representation. The single-precision result will consist essentially (i. e., except for some possible rounding and/or normalization procedure) of the first s of these

$2s$ digits. The rest of the result, if any, is the remainder. In the case of division, since the exact result may involve infinitely many digits, the remainder is usually given, as in the ordinary "long division" method, as a quantity which if divided by the original divisor with infinite precision would yield the remaining digits. In fixed-point addition and subtraction, properly scaled, there is no remainder. In floating-point addition and subtraction the presence of a nonzero remainder and the second set of s digits is indicated in an accessible register.

A properly written manual for a given digital computing machine will include a complete and unambiguous description of the result of executing an arithmetic operation for each such operation in the repertoire of the given machine. It should be possible from this to program a routine which will discover the presence of a nonzero remainder in each of the arithmetic operations, and which will also determine the sign of the difference between the machine single-precision result and the exact result in case of a nonzero remainder. With such a routine for examining remainders of machine single-precision arithmetic, we can then write "rounded-interval arithmetic" subroutines for the given computer based on the formulas (3–2). In place of the exact values for endpoints given by the equations (3–2), these subroutines would produce single-precision rounded endpoints, rounding positive right endpoints and negative left endpoints away from zero by addition of a low-order bit in case a nonzero remainder is present in the machine single-precision unrounded result, but not rounding negative right endpoints nor positive left endpoints nor any endpoints for which a zero remainder is detected in the unrounded single-precision machine result.

Such "rounded-interval arithmetic" routines have in fact been written and used on a number of machines.*

A computer program executed in rounded-interval arithmetic instead of ordinary machine arithmetic will result in a set of intervals represented by pairs of machine numbers such that each interval result contains the exact result of the corresponding infinite-precision arithmetic computations. Rounded-interval arithmetic keeps track of the accumulation in round-off error in any machine computation. Of course, the widths of the intervals computed in this way using a fixed word length for the machine-arithmetic computation of endpoints may grow quite large for a particular computation. We will give examples where it does and examples where it does not in the following sections. On the other hand, by making use of multiple-precision machine arithmetic for the computations of the end-points (with appropriate rounding of endpoints), intervals can be obtained

---

*A. Reiter [7] has written one for the CDC 1604 for use with FORTRAN 63 which enables the user to treat intervals as ordinary variables.

NOTE: The bracketed number designates a reference at the end of the chapter.

of arbitrarily narrow width for a given computation, i, e., a given finite sequence of arithmetic operations.

In the succeeding sections we will consider many nonarithmetic computations involving intervals, making use of intersections, unions, and other operations on intervals and interval-valued functions using analytical and set-theoretic techniques. Interval arithmetic by itself will not give us the upper and lower bounds to the exact solutions of most of the problems we are going to consider. But when used together with other techniques, analytical techniques involving interval-valued functions, interval arithmetic will play the role of permitting the programming of various algorithms which will use rounded-interval arithmetic in parts of the computations in order that error due to the finite precision of machine arithmetic and the propagation of error in initial data can be rigorously accounted for.

Rounded-interval arithmetic produces intervals which contain not only the infinite-precision results but also the unrounded machine-arithmetic results. Therefore an interval computed with rounded-interval arithmetic operations will provide a bound on the difference between the result of executing the same sequence of arithmetic operations with machine precision and with infinite precision. As a consequence, if a finite sequence of interval-arithmetic operations is going to produce intervals of narrow width, it is necessary that the corresponding computation in machine arithmetic would produce results close to those which would be obtained using exact real arithmetic.

*PROBLEM 3.7. Program rounded-interval arithmetic subroutines for a digital computer.

REFERENCES

1. BOCHE, R.E., "An operational interval arithmetic," presented at *IEEE National Electronics Conference,* Chicago, October 1963.
2. COLLINS, G., "Interval arithmetic for automatic error analysis," M & A-5, Mathematics and Applications Department, IBM (1960).
3. FISCHER, P. C., "Automatic propagated and round-off error analysis," *13*th *National Meeting of the A. C. M.,* 1958.
4. GIBB, A., "Procedures for range arithmetic," Algorithm 61, Comm. A. C. M., **4** : 7 (July 1961).
5. MOORE, R.E., "Automatic error analysis in digital computation," LMSD-48421, Lockheed Missiles and Space Co., Palo Alto, California, January 1959.
6. SUNAGA, T., "Theory; of an interval algebra and its application to numerical analysis," RAAG Memoirs II, Tokyo: Gakujutsu Bunken Fukyu-kai, 1958.

*An asterisk before a problem indicates that the problem involves programming or use of a digital computer.

7. REITER, A., "Interval arithmetic package (interval)," MRC Program #2, COOP Organ, Code-WISC, Mathematics Research Center, University of Wisconsin, Madison, Wisconsin.

8. YOUNG, R.C., "The algebra of many-valued quantities," *Math. Annalen*, **104** (1931), 260–290.

4 A METRIC TOPOLOGY FOR INTERVALS

We make $\mathscr{I}$ into a metric space by defining* the distance between a pair of intervals as the nonnegative function

$$d([a, b], [c, d]) = \max (|a - c|, |b - d|) \tag{4-1}$$

It is easy to see that

$$d(I, J) = d(J, I)$$

for any pair of intervals I, J.

It is also easy to see that

$$d(I, J) = 0$$

if and only if $I = J$.

The "triangle inequality," for $I, J, K \in \mathscr{I}$:

$$d(I, J) + d(J, K) \geq d(I, K) \tag{4-2}$$

follows easily from (4-1).

PROBLEM 4.1. Prove that (4-2) follows from (4-1).

Notice that $d([x, x], [y, y]) = |x - y|$ and therefore the metric d reduces to ordinary distance between two real numbers for degenerate intervals and so is consistent with our identification of a degenerate interval $[x, x]$ with the real number x. The real line is embedded "isometrically" in the metric space $(\mathscr{I}, d)$.

The space $\mathscr{I}$ of intervals can be visualized as a closed half-plane of

---

*We prefer this distance function to $\{(a - c)^2 + (b - d)^2\}^{1/2}$ (which would serve as well for most purposes), because it is simpler to compute.

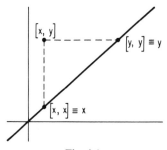

Fig. 4.1

points in the Euclidean (x, y)-plane above and including the diagonal $y = x$; see Fig. 4.1. (See, also, problems 2.3 and 2.4)

The points on the diagonal $y = x$ lying in the segment intercepted by the dotted sides of the triangle in Fig. 4.1 represent the real numbers contained in the interval $[x, y]$. The interval $[x, y]$ itself is represented by the point at the indicated vertex of the triangle.

Two interval numbers are close with respect to our distance function d, equation (4-1), if the corresponding points are close in the diagram.

We will use the notation $\mathscr{I}_{[a, b]} \equiv \mathscr{I}_A$, for an interval $A = [a, b]$, to mean the set of intervals which are contained in $[a, b]$,

$$\mathscr{I}_{[a,b]} = \{[x, y] | a \leq x \leq y \leq b\} \qquad (4\text{-}3)$$

or, in other words, $\mathscr{I}_{[a,b]}$ is the set of "subintervals" of $[a, b]$.

In Fig. 4.1, $\mathscr{I}_{[x,y]}$ is represented by the set of points making up the closed triangle between the vertex $[x, y]$ and the diagonal $y = x$.

A useful lemma in connection with the distance function was pointed out by C. T. Yang [2].

LEMMA 4.1. If $I, J \in \mathscr{I}$, and $\epsilon > 0$, then

$$d(I, J) \leq \epsilon \qquad (< \epsilon)$$

if and only if the following two statements hold :
(1) For every $x \in I$, there is a $y \in J$ such that $|x - y| \leq \epsilon \, (< \epsilon)$.
(2) For every $y \in J$, there is an $x \in I$ such that $|x - y| \leq \epsilon \, (< \epsilon)$.

Proof. Suppose $I = [a, b], J = [c, d] \in \mathscr{I}$, $\epsilon > 0$, and $d(I, J) \leq \epsilon$. To show that statements (1), (2) in Lemma 4.1 follow, consider an $x \in [a, b]$ and suppose that $|x - y| > \epsilon$ for *all* y in $[c, d]$. Then either $x < c - \epsilon$ or $x > d + \epsilon$; if $x < c - \epsilon$, then $a < c - \epsilon$ so $d([a, b], [c, d]) > \epsilon$ and a contradiction has been reached. Therefore we cannot have $|x - y| > \epsilon$ for *all* $y \in J$ so statement (1) is proved. Since $d(J, I) = d(I, J)$, statement (2) is also proved.

Going the other way, assume statements (1) and (2) are true; we want to show that $d(I, J) \leq \epsilon$. Suppose $d(I, J) > \epsilon$. Then either $|a - c| > \epsilon$ or $|b - d| > \epsilon$. If $c < a - \epsilon$, then there is no $x \in [a, b]$ such that $|x - c| \leq \epsilon$; if $a < c - \epsilon$, then there is no $y \in [c, d]$ such that $|y - a| \leq \epsilon$. The inequality $|b - d| > \epsilon$ also contradicts one of the statements (1) or (2). Therefore (1) and (2) together imply $d(I, J) \leq \epsilon$.

This completes the proof of Lemma 4.1.

LEMMA 4.2. In connection with studying the convergence of a nested sequence of intervals

$$X_1 \supset X_2 \supset \cdots \supset X_n \supset X_{n+1} \supset \cdots \supset A$$

to a particular interval A, it is useful sometimes to notice that if $I \subset J$ and $d(I, J) \leq \epsilon$, then $w(J) \leq w(I) + 2\epsilon$.

Of course, by the *convergence* of a sequence of intervals $A_1, A_2, \ldots$ to an interval I we mean that the sequence of real numbers $d(A_n, I)$ converges to zero, which amounts to saying that if $I = [a. b]$ and $A_n = [a_n, b_n]$, then $a_n \to a$ and $b_n \to b$.

In studying the construction of algorithms for the computation in a finite number of machine operations of intervals containing exact solutions of various problems in analysis, we will usually seek algorithms which can be executed by the machine to produce, say, an interval result X depending on a number of parameters (such as the number of binary digits carried in the machine arithmetic used by the rounded-interval arithmetic subroutines, the number of terms in a truncated series to be used, and so on), so that we will have $X(p_1, p_2, \ldots, p_N) \supset S$, where S is the set of exact solutions for some problem in analysis corresponding to initial data lying in certain intervals.

If possible, we would like the algorithms to have the property that $X(p_1, p_2, \ldots, p_N)$ converges to S for a sequence of sets of values of the parameters $p_1, p_2, \ldots, p_N$; and we would even like the machine program involved with X to be able to choose appropriate values of $p_1, p_2, \ldots, p_N$ during the course of its execution on the computer so that X comes within a specified distance of S. Granted these things, we would still further like the resulting computation to be as efficient as possible. As we shall see in subsequent chapters, it is sometimes possible to program an approximate determination of a set of values of $p_1, p_2, \ldots, p_N$ which minimizes the computation time required to find an X such that $d(X, S) \leq \epsilon$.

Lemma 4.2 above can be seen by considering Fig. 4.2. The shaded square represents the set of points I such that $I \subset J$ and $d(I, J) \leq \epsilon$. Clearly $w(I) \geq w(J) - 2\epsilon$.

We denote the "Cartesian product" of two sets S_1, S_2 by $S_1 \otimes S_2$, if $x \in S_1, y \in S_2$, then $(x, y) \in S_1 \otimes S_2$.

We will represent the statement: "f is a function defined on elements

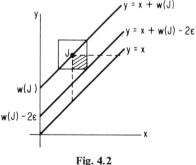

Fig. 4.2

of a set S (S is called the "domain" of definition of f) and having values in a set T" (T is called the "range space" of f) symbolically by $f: S \to T$. If $x \in S$, then $f(x) \in T$. If we denote the real numbers by R, then $d : \mathcal{I} \otimes \mathcal{I} \to R$, where d is given in equation (4-1).

Our introduction of a metric in $\mathcal{I}$ given by the distance function d, equation (4-1), allows us to consider *continuous interval-valued functions*.

For example, if (M, ρ) is a metric space with distance function $\rho : M \otimes M \to R$, then an interval-valued function $f: M \to \mathcal{I}$ defined on M is continuous at $x_1 \in M$ if and only if for every $\epsilon > 0$ there is a $\delta > 0$ such that for all $x_2 \in M$, $\rho(x_1, x_2) < \delta$ implies $d(f(x_1), f(x_2)) < \epsilon$. And f is *uniformly continuous* in M if and only if for every $\epsilon > 0$ there is a $\delta > 0$ such that for all $x_1, x_2 \in M$, $\rho(x_1, x_2) < \delta$ implies $d(f(x_1), f(x_2)) < \epsilon$.

If $f: I \to \mathcal{I}$ is a continuous real-valued (degenerate intervals) or even a continuous interval-valued function on a closed real interval I, then there is a natural extension of f to an interval-valued function on $\mathcal{I}_I$. In fact, we define the *united extension*, $\bar{f}$, (see Strother [4] and [5]) of f by

$$\bar{f}: \mathcal{I}_I \to \mathcal{I}$$

with

$$\bar{f}(x) = \bigcup_{x \in X} f(x) \qquad \text{for } X \in \mathcal{I}_I$$

That is, $\bar{f}(X)$ is the union of the values $f(x)$ for x in the subinterval X of the interval I.

Points in $\mathcal{I} \otimes \mathcal{I} \otimes \cdots \otimes \mathcal{I}$ are *interval vectors* $(X_1, X_2, \ldots, X_n)$. We define the *distance* between two *interval vectors* $(X_1, X_2, \ldots, X_n), (Y_1, Y_2, \ldots, Y_n)$ as $\max_i d(X_i, Y_i)$, thus making $\mathcal{I} \otimes \mathcal{I} \otimes \cdots \otimes \mathcal{I}$ into a metric space.

If $f: I_1 \otimes I_2 \otimes \cdots \otimes I_n \to \mathcal{I}$ is a continuous interval-valued function on the Cartesian product of the intervals $I_1, \ldots, I_n$, we call $\bar{f}$ the *united extension* of f with

$$\bar{f}: \mathcal{I}_{I_1} \otimes \mathcal{I}_{I_2} \otimes \cdots \otimes \mathcal{I}_{I_n} \to \mathcal{I}$$

defined by $\bar{f}(X_1, X_2, \ldots, X_n) = \cup f(x_1, x_2, \ldots, x_n)$, with the union taken over $x_i \in X_i, i = 1, 2, \ldots, n$.

The value of the function $\bar{f}: \mathcal{I}_I \to \mathcal{I}$ at a point X in its domain of definition is the union of the intervals (or real numbers) in the image of X under the mapping $f: I \to \mathcal{I}$. For a real-valued function $f: I \to R$, this is sometimes written $\bar{f}(X) = \{f(x) | x \in X\}$. We use the special notation $\bar{f}$, in particular with $\bar{f}(X) = \{f(x) | x \in X\}$ for a continuous real-valued function f, in order to emphasize the fact that $\bar{f}$ is a *single-valued* function whose value is a *point* in $\mathcal{I}$, that is, an interval number.

THEOREM 4.1. If $I_1, I_2, \ldots, I_n \in \mathscr{I}$ and $f: I_1 \otimes I_2 \otimes \cdots \otimes I_n \to \mathscr{I}$ is continuous, then the united extension $\bar{f}: \mathscr{I}_{I_1} \otimes \mathscr{I}_{I_2} \cdots \otimes \mathscr{I}_{I_n} \to \mathscr{I}$ is continuous.

Proof. Strother [5] proves that if X, Y are compact Hausdorff spaces and $f: X \to Y$ is continuous, then the united extension $\bar{f}$ is also continuous. The topology there includes ours for $\mathscr{I}$. We give the following proof for our more special theorem.

Let $\epsilon > 0$, $X_i \in I_i$, $X_i' \in I_i$ for $i = 1, 2, \ldots, n$. Since f is continuous, there is a $\delta > 0$ such that $x_i \in X_i$, $x_i' \in X_i'$, $i = 1, 2, \ldots, n$ with $|x_i - x_i'| < \delta$ implies $d(f(x_1, \ldots, x_n), f(x_1', \ldots, x_n')) > \epsilon$. Note that the continuity of f implies *uniform* continuity on the compact domain of definition given for f (see [3]). Now by Lemma 4.1, $d(\bar{f}(P_1), \bar{f}(P_2)) < \epsilon$ if and only if for each $t \in \bigcup_{p \in P_1} f(p)$ there is a $t' \in \bigcup_{p' \in P_2} f(p')$ with $|t - t'| < \epsilon$ and for each t' there is a t (with the same properties). We are abbreviating $(x_1, \ldots, x_2)$ by p and $(X_1, \ldots, X_n)$ by P. Now $t \in \bigcup_{p \in P_1} f(p)$ implies that $t \in f(p)$ for some choice of $x_i \in X_i$, so $d(X_i, X_i') < \delta$ implies $|x_i - x_i'| < \delta$ and therefore $d(f(p), f(p')) < \epsilon$ for $p \in P_1, p' \in P_2$. Therefore there is a $t' \in f(p')$ with $p' \in P_2$ such that $|t - t'| < \epsilon$. And similarly for a $t' \in \bigcup_{p' \in P_2} f(p')$ there is a t in $f(p)$ (and hence in $\bigcup_{p \in P_1} f(p)$) such that $|t - t'| < \epsilon$. This completes the proof of Theorem 4.1.

THEOREM 4.2. The arithmetic operations on $\mathscr{I}$ defined by (3–1) are continuous except for division by intervals containing zero.

Proof. What we are saying is that as functions of two variables, the arithmetic operations in $\mathscr{I}$,

$$+ (X_1, X_2) \equiv X_1 + X_2, \quad \text{and so on}$$

are continuous interval-valued function on $\mathscr{I} \otimes \mathscr{I}$ (division by $X_2, 0 \in X_2$, excepted).

Using Theorem 4.1, the proof is exceedingly simple.

From (3–1) the interval arithmetic operations *are* the united extensions of the real arithmetic operations. The real arithmetic operations are continuous. By Theorem 4.1, therefore, so are the interval arithmetic operations continuous. This completes the proof of Theorem 4.2.

Perhaps a remark should be added on the above proof. In Theorem 4.1, the domain of f is supposed to be compact, e.g., $I_1 \otimes I_2$ for some intervals I_1, I_2. On the other hand the real arithmetic operations are defined on all pairs of real numbers (except $\div 0$). There is no difficulty, however, since any pair of intervals (I_1, I_2) is in the interior of $\mathscr{I}_{I_1'} \otimes \mathscr{I}_{I_2'}$ for some $I_1', I_2' \in \mathscr{I}$, and if $0 \notin I_2$ then I_2' may also be chosen with $0 \notin I_2'$.

It is not hard to show that the constant interval functions and the "projections," i.e., functions of the type

$$F_\kappa: \mathscr{I} \otimes \mathscr{I} \otimes \cdots \otimes \mathscr{I} \to \mathscr{I}$$

with $F_\kappa(X_1, X_2, \ldots, X_n) = X_\kappa$, $1 \le \kappa \le n$, are continuous. We conclude the following theorem, using theorem 4.2 and finite induction.

THEOREM 4.3. *Rational interval functions* are continuous.

By a *rational interval function* we mean a function

$$F: \mathscr{I}_{I_1} \otimes \mathscr{I}_{I_n} \otimes \cdots \otimes \mathscr{I}_{I_n} \to \mathscr{I}$$

such that there is a rational expression in the interval variables $X_1, X_2, \ldots,$ X_n which represents the values $F(X_1, X_2, \ldots, X_n)$ of F (see Theorem 3.1). Since their domains are compact by definition, rational interval functions are, in fact, *uniformly* continuous.

By definition the value of $F(X_1, X_2, \ldots, X_n)$ is an interval in $\mathscr{I}$ for every set of arguments $(X_1, X_2, \ldots, X_n)$ in its compact domain, therefore $|F|$ is bounded. It the previous chapters we have shown that evaluation of a rational expression in interval arithmetic gives a direct computation of upper and lower bounds to the range of values of the corresponding real rational function, but that the bounds are usually not sharp, i.e., the intervals between the lower and upper bounds computed this way are wider than the actual range of values of the real rational expression.

We proceed now to describe a very general convergence theorem which provides, in principle, for the computation of intervals containing and *arbitrarily close* to the actual range of values of a real rational function of n real variables when each real variable ranges over some interval of values.

The idea is as follows : rather than substitute the whole interval $[a, b]$ for a variable X in an expression and then evaluate using interval arithmetic, we can first *subdivide* the interval $[a, b]$ into *subintervals*

$$[a, b] = [a, a_1] \cup [a_1, a_2] \cup \cdots \cup [a_n, b]$$

say of equal width $(b - a)/(n + 1)$, then evaluate the expression in question in interval arithmetic for each of the subintervals, and finally compute the union of the resulting partial ranges of values. Symbolically, if f is a real function, $f : R \to R$

$$\{f(x)|x \in [a, b]\} = \bigcup_{i=0}^{n} \{f(x)|x \in [a_i, a_{i+1}]\} \tag{4-4}$$

with $a_0 = a, a_{n+1} = b$. In particular, if F is a rational interval function corresponding to a real rational function f such that on degenerate intervals, or real numbers, we have $F([x, x]) \equiv F(x) \equiv f(x)$ (f is called the *real restriction* of F), then from Theorem 3.1 we have

$$F([a, b]) \supset \{f(x) | x \in [a, b]\}$$

and also

$$F([a_i, a_{i+1}]) \supset \{(f(x) | x \in [a_i, a_{i+1}]\}$$

so

$$\bigcup_{i=0}^{n} F([a_i, a_{i+1}]) \supset \{f(x) | x \in [a, b]\} \qquad (4\text{-}5)$$

The theorem we are going to prove states that as $n \to \infty$ the computable expression

$$\bigcup_{i=0}^{n} F([a_i, a_{i+1}])$$

in fact *converges* to $\{f(x) | x \in [a, b]\}$.

Actually we want to prove a little more—namely, something about the *rate* of convergence.

PROBLEM 4.2. Show that equation (4-4) is true.

PROBLEM 4.3. Subdivide [0, 1] into 2, 3, 4 subintervals of equal width and, using (4-5), compute intervals containing

$$\{f(x) = x(1 - x) | 0 \le x \le 1\}$$

What is the width of the union (4-5) in this problem as a function of n?

The convergence of the unions in (4-5) is made plausible geometrically by considering Fig. 4.3. From Theorem 4.3, we know that the rational interval function F is continuous, so its value at $[a_i, a_{i+1}]$ is close to its value at a real number $x_i \in [a_i, a_{i+1}]$ if x_i is close (with respect to the distance function d) to the whole subinterval $[a_i, a_{i+1}]$. From Fig. 4.3, we can see that this will be the case for large n. In fact we have :

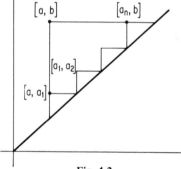

Fig. 4.3

THEOREM 4.4. Let $F: \mathscr{I}_{A_1} \otimes \mathscr{I}_{A_2} \otimes \cdots \otimes_{A_n} \to \mathscr{I}$ be a rational interval function and let f be the *real* restriction of F, i.e., for $x_i \in A_i$,

$$F([x_1, x_1], [x_2, x_2], \ldots, [x_n, x_n]) \equiv f(x_1, x_2, \ldots, x_n)$$

Notice that since $|F|$ is bounded in its domain, then the real restriction of F, namely f, cannot have any singularities for $x_i \in A_i, i = 1, 2, \ldots, n$. In fact f is also bounded.

Let $\bar{f}$ be the united extension of f, i.e., for $X_i \subset A_i$,

$$\bar{f}(X_1, X_2, \ldots, X_n) = \{f(x_1, x_2, \ldots, x_n) | x_i \in X_i, i = 1, 2, \ldots, n\}$$

Subdivide each of the intervals X_i so that

$$X_i = \bigcup_{j=1}^{N} X_{i,j} \qquad \text{with } w(X_{i,j}) = \frac{1}{N} w(X_i)$$

There is a positive real number K such that

$$\bigcup F(X_{1,j_1}, X_{2,j_2}, \ldots, X_{n,j_n}) = \bar{f}(X_1, X_2, \ldots, X_n) + E_N \qquad (4\text{-}6)$$

with the union taken over $j_1, j_2, \ldots, j_n$ running independently over the integers $1, 2, \ldots, N$, and where E_N is an interval such that $0 \in E_N$ and $w(E_N) \leq K/N \max_i w(X_i)$.

Proof. The statement $0 \in E_N$ in connection with equation (4-6) asserts that the range of values

$$\{f(x_1, x_2, \ldots, x_n) | x_i \in X_i, i = 1, 2, \ldots, n\}$$

is contained in the union in (4-6). This follows from Theorem 3.1 and the fact that for *any* function f on *any* set S written in *any* way as a union, $S = \bigcup S_i$, we have

$$\{f(x) | x \in S\} = \bigcup \{f(x) | x \in S_i\} \qquad (4\text{-}7)$$

What we have still to prove is that

$$w(E_N) \leq \frac{K}{N} \max_i w(X_i)$$

From Theorem 3.1 and Lemma 4.2 we know that there is an interval $E_{j_1, j_2, \ldots, j_n}$ such that

$$F(X_{1,j_2}, \ldots, X_{n,j_n}) = \bar{f}(X_{1,j_2}, \ldots, X_{n,j_n}) + E_{j_1, j_2, \ldots, j_n}$$

with $0 \in E_{j_1, j_2, \ldots, j_n}$.

If $E_N = \bigcup E_{j_1, j_2, \ldots, j_n}$, then $|E_N| = \max |E_{j_1, j_2, \ldots, j_n}|$ (see Chapter 2 for $|[a, b]| = \max(|a|, |b|)$) and $w(E_N) \leq 2|E_N|$ (because $b - a \leq |a| + |b|$), so it is sufficient to show that

$$|E_{j_1, j_2, \ldots, j_n}| = d(F(X_{1\,j_1}, \ldots, X_{n,j_n}), \bar{f}(X_{1,j_1}, \ldots, X_{n,j_n}))$$

$$\leq \frac{K}{2N} \max_i w(X_i) \qquad (4\text{-}8)$$

for some $K > 0$ independent of $N, j_1, j_2, \ldots, j_n$.

In the rational interval expression for $F(X_1, \ldots, X_n)$ each variable X_i occurs only a finite number of times (possibly zero). In each occurrence substitute a new variable $X_i^{(p)}$, $p = 1, 2, \ldots, p_i$. After substitution of the variables $X_i^{(p)}$ we obtain a new rational interval expression

$$H(X_1^{(1)}, X_1^{(2)}, \ldots, X_1^{(P_1)}, X_2^{(1)}, \ldots, X_n^{(P_n)})$$

There may be also a finite number of interval constants $C_1, \ldots, C_q$ in the expressions for F and H.

For each choice of real numbers $c_1, c_2, \ldots, c_q$ from the intervals C_1, $\ldots, C_q, c_m \in C_m$, there is a real rational function $h_c, c = (c_1, c_2, \ldots, c_q)$; the functions h_c satisfy

$$\bigcup_{\substack{c_m \in C_m \\ m=1,2,\ldots,q}} h_c(x_1^{(1)}, x_1^{(2)}, \ldots, x_n^{(P_n)}) = \bar{h}(x_1^{(1)}, x_1^{(2)}, \ldots, x_n^{(P_n)})$$

where $\bar{h}$ is the united extension of h, and h is the real restriction of H.

The set of rational functions h_c is uniformly bounded (i.e., for $c_m \in C_{m_1}$, $m = 1, 2, \ldots, q$) and has a uniform Lipschitz constant on its compact domain of definition; thus, there is a positive real number $K/2$ independent of c such that for all $x_i, x_i^{(p)} \in x_i, i = 1, 2, \ldots, n, p = 1, 2, \ldots, P_n$

$$|h_c(x_1^{(1)}, \ldots, x_1^{(P_1)}; \ldots; x_n^{(1)}, \ldots, x_n^{(P_n)})$$

$$- h_c(x_1, \ldots, x_1; \ldots; x_n, \ldots, x_n)| \leq \frac{K}{2} \max_{i,p} |x_i^{(p)} - x_i| \qquad (4\text{-}9)$$

Since each variable in the expression H occurs only once, we have, because of a remark in Chapter 3,

$$H(X_1, \ldots, X_1; \ldots; X_n, \ldots, X_n)$$

$$= \bigcup_{x_i^{(p)} \in X_i} \bar{h}(x_1^{(1)}, \ldots, x_1^{(P_1)}; \ldots; x_n^{(1)}, \ldots, x_n^{(P_n)})$$

From the construction of H, we have

$$F(X_1, X_2, \ldots, X_n) = H(X_1, \ldots, X_1; \ldots; X_n, \ldots, X_n)$$

and

$$\bar{f}(X_1, \ldots, X_n) = \bar{h}(X_1, \ldots, X_1; \ldots; X_n, \ldots, X_n)$$

with $\max_{x_i^{(p)}, x_i \in x_i} |x_i^{(p)} - x_i| = w(X_i)$.

Since (4-9) also holds for $x_i, x_i^{(p)} \in X_{i,j}$ with the right-hand side of the inequality replaced by

$$\frac{K}{2} \max_{i,p} |x_i^{(p)} - x_i| = \frac{K}{2} w(X_{i,j})$$

$$= \frac{K}{2N} w(X_i)$$

we obtain (4-8) and the theorem is proved.

In the special case of $n = 1, N = 1$, we have the following useful corollaries:

COROLLARY 1 TO THEOREM 4.4. For a real-valued real restriction f of a rational interval function F on $\mathscr{I}_A$ there is a $K > 0$ such that $X \subset A$ implies

$$F(X) = \bar{f}(X) + E \quad \text{with } w(E) \leq Kw(X) \text{ and } 0 \in E$$

COROLLARY 2 TO THEOREM 4.4. For a rational interval function F on $\mathscr{I}_A$ with a real restriction which is real-valued there is a positive K such that $X \subset A$ implies $w(F(X)) \leq Kw(X)$.

Corollary 1 follows directly from Theorem 4.4; corollary 2 uses the additional fact that the real restriction f (of F) satisfies a Lipschitz condition in A.

In the introduction of the discussion on the convergence of unions of interval functions on subintervals we stated that *in principle* the procedure provides for the computation of intervals arbitrarily close to exact ranges of values of real rational functions. The method is mainly of theoretical interest.

In practice, since the convergence is only linear in the number of subdivisions in *each* interval variable, for a function of many variables a very large number of evaluations would be required to obtain a small residual or excess width. For n variables, to make the excess width less than ϵ would take something like $(1/\epsilon)^n$ evaluations of a rational interval function.

In Chapter 6 we take up some more efficient ways of bounding the range of values of rational functions.

REFERENCES

1. KELLEY. J. L., *General Topology*. Princeton, N. J.: D. Van Nostrand Co., Inc., 1955.
2. MOORE, R. E., and YANG, C. T., "Interval analysis," LMSD-285875, Lockheed Missiles and Space Co., Palo Alto, California (1959).
3. MOORE, R. E., "Interval arithmetic and automatic error analysis in digital computing," Applied Math. & Stat. Lab., Stanford University Technical Report No. 25 (1962) (also Ph.D. dissertation, Stanford University, October 1962).
4. STROTHER, W., "Continuous multi-valued Functions," *Bol. Soc. Mat.*, São Paulo, **10** (1958), 87–120.
5. STROTHER, W., "Fixed points, fixed sets, and *M*-retracts," *Duke. Math. J.*, **22** : 4 (1955), 551–556.

5 MATRIX COMPUTATIONS WITH INTERVALS

5.1 DIRECT METHODS

Besides evaluation of polynomials and rational functions, there are other commonly occuring computational problems which require only finite sequences of arithmetic operations for their solution such as the computation of inner products of vectors, sums and products of matrices, inversion of matrices, and the solution of linear algebraic systems—for example, by the Gaussian elimination process.

If exact initial values are given, then the only source of error is round-off, i.e., error due to the finite precision of machine arithmetic. Otherwise, we have also the propagation of error in the initial data.

In either case, interval arithmetic furnishes a direct means of computing intervals containing each component of the exact solution.

By an *interval vector* we mean a vector whose components are interval numbers. Similarly, by an *interval matrix* we mean a matrix whose elements are interval numbers.

In his book, *Linear Computations* [1], and also in a recent paper [2], P. S. Dwyer has discussed matrix computations using interval arithmetic (or "range arithmetic").

If $(u_1, u_2, \ldots, u_n)$ and $(v_1, v_2, \ldots, v_n)$ are interval vectors then the inner product $p = u_1 v_1 + u_2 v_2 + \cdots + u_n v_n$ can be computed in interval arithmetic (or in rounded interval arithmetic, by the machine) resulting in an interval containing all the real numbers defined by values of the inner product of real vectors u and v with real elements from the given intervals $u_1, u_2, \ldots, u_n, v_1, v_2, \ldots, v_n$. In fact, using exact-interval arithmetic, the actual range of values of the inner product of the real vectors will be computed, since we are supposing here that each component of the real vectors is allowed to range independently over its interval of values.

More generally, it is clear from the definition of interval arithmetic given by equation (3–1) that the evaluation of any rational expression in interval arithmetic in which each variable *occurs only once** will produce the exact range of values of the real rational function defined by the expression.

In particular, the product of two interval matrices using interval arithmetic is again an interval matrix consisting of interval elements each of which is exactly the range of values of the corresponding element of the product of a pair of real matrices whose elements are chosen independently from the corresponding elements of the interval matrices.

To find the set of solutions of a linear system of order one

$$ax = b$$

corresponding to intervals of values of the coefficients, say $a \in A$, $b \in B$, we can compute B/A using interval arithmetic and obtain the set of real numbers b/a with $a \in A$, $b \in B$ [see equation (3–1)].

The situation is different for systems of order higher than one. Consider the system of order two

$$a_{11}x_1 + a_{12}x_2 = b_1$$
$$a_{21}x_1 + a_{22}x_2 = b_2$$

with $a_{ij} \in A_{ij}$ for $i, j = 1, 2$ and $b_j \in B_j$ for $j = 1, 2$.

Using the Gaussian elimination process, we can rewrite the system as

$$a_{11}x_1 + a_{12}x_2 = b_1$$
$$(a_{11}a_{22} - a_{21}a_{12})x_2 = a_{11}b_2 - a_{21}b_1$$

If $a_{11}a_{22} - a_{21}a_{12} \neq 0$, then

$$x_2 = \frac{a_{11}b_2 - a_{21}b_1}{a_{11}a_{22} - a_{21}a_{12}}$$

and if $a_{11} \neq 0$, then

$$x_1 = \left(\frac{1}{a_{11}}\right)(b_1 - a_{12}x_2)$$

Of course, by rearranging rows or columns of the coefficients we can insure that $a_{11} \neq 0$ if the matrix of coefficients is nonsingular, so that this condition on a_{11} is not essentially restrictive. Alternatively, using Cramer's rule, x_1 can be expressed as

$$x_1 = \frac{b_1a_{22} - b_2a_{12}}{a_{11}a_{22} - a_{12}a_{21}}$$

---

*See the remark at the end of Section 3.1.

The set of solution vectors, i.e., the interval vector of solutions, has components

$$X_1 = \left\{ \frac{b_1 a_{22} - b_2 a_{12}}{a_{11} a_{22} - a_{12} a_{21}} \middle| a_{ij} \in A_{ij}, b_j \in B_j, i, j = 1, 2 \right\}$$

$$X_2 = \left\{ \frac{b_2 a_{11} - b_1 a_{21}}{a_{11} a_{22} - a_{12} a_{21}} \middle| a_{ij} \in A_{ij}, b_j \in B_j, i, j = 1, 2 \right\}$$

$$(5\text{-}1)$$

If $A_{11} = A_{21} = 1$, $A_{12} = 2$, $A_{22} = [10, 12]$, $B_1 = 1$, $B_2 = 0$, then

$$X_1 = \left\{ \frac{a_{22}}{a_{22} - 2} \middle| a_{22} \in [10, 12] \right\}$$

$$X_2 = \left\{ \frac{-1}{a_{22} - 2} \middle| a_{22} \in [10, 12] \right\}$$

The function $a_{22}/(a_{22} - 2)$ is monotonic decreasing in the interval $10 \leq a_{22} < 12$ so that

$$X_1 = \left[\frac{12}{10}, \frac{10}{8} \right] = [1\tfrac{1}{5}, 1\tfrac{1}{4}]$$

For X_2, we find that $X_2 = [-\tfrac{1}{8}, -\tfrac{1}{10}]$. If we evaluate the expression

$$\frac{-1}{A_{22} - 2} = \frac{-1}{[10, 12] - 2}$$

in interval arithmetic, we obtain $[-\tfrac{1}{8}, -\tfrac{1}{10}]$ which is exactly the range of the solution component X_2.

However, if we evaluate the expression

$$\frac{A_{22}}{A_{22} - 2} = \frac{[10, 12]}{[10, 12] - 2}$$

in interval arithmetic, we obtain

$$\frac{[10, 12]}{[8, 10]} = [1, 1\tfrac{1}{2}]$$

which *contains* the exact range of values of $a_{22}/(a_{22} - 2)$, namely $[1\tfrac{1}{5}, 1\tfrac{1}{4}]$, as it *must*; but the interval arithmetic result is a wider interval than the exact range of values.

At the point where the substitution of the numerical interval $[10, 12]$ is made for the variable A_{22}, the identity of the variable in its two occurrences in the expression is lost. From the point of view of the arithmetic alone, the computation $[10, 12]/([10, 12] - 2)$ could just as well be the evaluation of the range of values of a function of two independent variables

$$\left\{ \frac{x}{y - 2} \middle| x \in [10, 12], y \in [10, 12] \right\}$$

in which case the correct range of values is the interval $[1, 1\tfrac{1}{2}]$.

In the particular example at hand, we have

$$\frac{a_{22}}{a_{22} - 2} = \frac{a_{22} - 2}{a_{22} - 2} + \frac{2}{a_{22} - 2} = 1 + \frac{2}{a_{22} - 2}$$

so that the expression $1 + 2/(a_{22} - 2)$ is equivalent (in real arithmetic) and contains only a single occurrence of the variable a_{22}. Thus, if we evaluate

$$1 + \frac{2}{A_{22} - 2} = 1 + \frac{2}{[10, 12] - 2}$$

in interval arithmetic, we obtain

$$1 + \frac{2}{[8, 10]} = 1 + [\tfrac{1}{5}, \tfrac{1}{4}] = [1\tfrac{1}{5}, 1\tfrac{1}{4}]$$

which is the exact range of values.

In general, it is not possible to rewrite a rational expression in which a number of real variables each occur several times in such a way that the new expression contains only one occurrence of each variable.

Consider, for example, the expression

$$\frac{a_{22} + a_{12}}{a_{22} - a_{12}}$$

corresponding to setting $B_1 = 1, B_2 = -1, A_{11} = 1, A_{21} = 1$ in equation (5-1) for X_1. Thus

$$X_1 = \left\{ \frac{a_{22} + a_{12}}{a_{22} - a_{12}} \middle| a_{12} \in A_{12}, a_{22} \in A_{22} \right\} \tag{5-2}$$

PROBLEM 5.1.

a. What is the actual interval of values of X_1 in equation (5-2) for $A_{12} = [5, 10], A_{22} = [1, 2]$?

b. Using $(A_{22} + A_{12})/(A_{22} - A_{12})$, or any rational expression which is equivalent with respect to evaluation in *real* arithmetic, substitute the interval numbers $[5, 10]$ for A_{12} and $[1, 2]$ for A_{22} and evaluate in interval arithmetic.

For a nonsingular n-by-n real matrix, A, and an n-vector, b, the linear algebraic system of order n for the n-vector, x, can be written

$$Ax = b \tag{5-3}$$

and has the solution $x = A^{-1}b$.

If we have a method for computing an interval matrix M such that each element of M is an interval containing the range of values of the corresponding element of A^{-1} when the elements of A vary independently over certain intervals, then by multiplying an interval vector B by the matrix M using interval arithmetic we will obtain a vector each of whose components is an interval containing the possible values of the corresponding component of the solution of equation (5-3) when the components of b are allowed to vary over the interval components of B.

If B and C are interval vectors, then by $B \subset C$ we mean that each component of B is an interval contained in the corresponding interval component of C. Similarly, for interval matrices A and M, by $A \subset M$, we mean that each interval element of A is contained in the corresponding interval element of M.

Direct methods (i.e., ones involving only a finite number of arithmetic operations to obtain the exact result, assuming infinite-precision arithmetic) for computing the inverse of a matrix can be based, for example, on Gaussian elimination; putting a special vector for b in equation (5–3) consisting of a single one in some component and zeros in the rest, a column of the inverse matrix can be found.

If the matrix A in equation (5–3) has exactly known real elements, then by using such a direct method with rounded-interval arithmetic an interval matrix can be found with arbitrarily narrow interval elements containing the exact elements of the inverse matrix A^{-1} by using *high enough precision* in the machine arithmetic upon which the computation of the endpoints of the intervals concerned is based, i.e., by going to multiple-precision rounded-interval arithmetic.

On the other hand, if A is an interval matrix, then computation of A^{-1} by a direct method using even exact, i.e., infinite-precision, interval arithmetic will usually yield a resulting interval matrix with elements which are wider than the actual range of values. Also, the use of a *fixed machine precision* in rounded-interval arithmetic for the inversion of matrices, even with exactly known real elements, by a direct method introduces intervals of coefficients during the elimination process—for example, in transforming the original matrix to upper-triangular form. In many cases, the multiple occurrence of interval elements in the expressions for the transformed coefficients produces growth of the widths of the containing intervals much beyond the actual accumulation of rounding error in the corresponding results using ordinary machine arithmetic.

*PROBLEM 5.2. Using rounded-interval arithmetic subroutines for the execution of arithmetic operations, invert some matrices with known inverses using a direct method on the computer. With the same program invert some interval matrices.

For the purpose of providing a numerical comparison with the methods of the next section we will give some examples now of the inversion of two-by-two interval matrices using a direct method. We suppose that

$$A = \begin{pmatrix} a_{11} & a_{12} \\ a_{21} & a_{22} \end{pmatrix}$$

is a nonsingular real matrix. Solving first the system

$$a_{11} x_1^{(1)} + a_{12} x_2^{(1)} = 1$$
$$a_{21} x_1^{(1)} + a_{22} x_2^{(1)} = 0$$

by Gaussian elimination, assuming here that $a_{11} \neq 0$, we obtain first

$$a_{11} x_1^{(1)} + a_{12} x_2^{(1)} = 1$$
$$(a_{11} a_{22} - a_{21} a_{12}) x_2^{(1)} = -a_{21}$$

so that

$$x_2^{(1)} = \frac{-a_{21}}{a_{11} a_{22} - a_{21} a_{12}}$$

$$x_1^{(1)} = \frac{1}{a_{11}} (1 - a_{12} x_2^{(1)})$$

Now

$$\begin{pmatrix} x_1^{(1)} \\ x_2^{(1)} \end{pmatrix} = \begin{pmatrix} (A^{-1})_{11} & (A^{-1})_{12} \\ (A^{-1})_{21} & (A^{-1})_{22} \end{pmatrix} \begin{pmatrix} 1 \\ 0 \end{pmatrix} = \begin{pmatrix} (A^{-1})_{11} \\ (A^{-1})_{21} \end{pmatrix}$$

Similarly, solving the system

$$a_{11} x_1^{(2)} + a_{12} x_2^{(2)} = 0$$
$$a_{21} x_1^{(2)} + a_{22} x_2^{(2)} = 1$$

we obtain

$$x_2^{(2)} = \frac{a_{11}}{a_{22} a_{11} - a_{21} a_{12}} = (A^{-1})_{22}$$

$$x_1^{(2)} = \frac{1}{a_{11}} (-a_{12} x_2^{(2)}) = (A^{-1})_{12}$$

Summarizing these formulas, we can write

$$A^{-1} = \begin{pmatrix} (A^{-1})_{11} & (A^{-1})_{12} \\ (A^{-1})_{21} & (A^{-1})_{22} \end{pmatrix}$$

with

$$(A^{-1})_{22} = \frac{a_{11}}{a_{22} a_{11} - a_{21} a_{12}} \tag{5-4}$$

$$(A^{-1})_{12} = \frac{1}{a_{11}} (-a_{12}(A^{-1})_{22}) \tag{5-5}$$

$$(A^{-1})_{21} = \frac{-a_{21}}{a_{11} a_{22} - a_{21} a_{12}} \tag{5-6}$$

$$(A^{-1})_{11} = \frac{1}{a_{11}} (1 - a_{12}(A^{-1})_{21}) \tag{5-7}$$

Clearly, if we replace the real arithmetic operations in the formulas (5-4), (5-5), (5-6), (5-7) by interval arithmetic operations (or rounded-interval arithmetic operations) and the real variables a_{11}, a_{12}, a_{21}, a_{22} by interval variables M_{11}, M_{12}, M_{21}, M_{22}, we obtain formulas for intervals which contain the range of possible values of the inverse A^{-1} of any real matrix with elements $a_{11} \in M_{11}$, $a_{12} \in M_{12}$, $a_{21} \in M_{21}$, $a_{22} \in M_{22}$. A singular matrix A will cause an attempted division by an interval containing zero for any M containing A (i.e., $A_{ij} \in M_{ij}$).

As a first numerical example, take the real matrix

$$A = \begin{pmatrix} 3 & 1 \\ 3 & 2 \end{pmatrix} \tag{5-8}$$

Using the formulas (3-2) in Chapter 3 for endpoints and using three-significant-decimal-digit rounded arithmetic based on those endpoint formulas, we obtain the following interval matrix containing A^{-1}:

$$A^{-1} \subset \begin{pmatrix} [.662, .672] & [-.338, -.332] \\ [-1.01, -.999] & [.999, 1.01] \end{pmatrix} \tag{5-9}$$

The details of the computation of the first element of the matrix displayed on the right-hand side of (5-9) are as follows (using three-place rounded-interval arithmetic):

From (5-8) we have

$$a_{11} = 3, \quad a_{12} = 1, \quad a_{21} = 3, \quad a_{22} = 2$$

Using (5-6) we get

$$a_{11}a_{22} - a_{21}a_{12} \in [3.00, 3.00]$$

(no rounding was needed). We then compute [see equation (3-1)]

$$\frac{1}{a_{11}a_{22} - a_{21}a_{12}} \in [.333, .334]$$

and

$$(A^{-1})_{21} = \frac{-a_{21}}{a_{11}a_{22} - a_{21}a_{12}} \in [-3.00, -3.00][.333, .334]$$

$$= [-1.002, -.999]$$

or

$$(A^{-1})_{21} \in [-1.002, -.999] \subset [-1.01, -.999]$$

(to three figures). Going to equation (5-7), we obtain

$$a_{12}(A^{-1})_{21} \in [1.00, 1.00][-1.01, -.999] \subset [-1.01, -.999]$$

and

$$1 - a_{12}(A^{-1})_{21} \in [1.999, 2.01] \subset [1.99, 2.01]$$

and

$$\frac{1}{a_{11}} \in [.333, .334]$$

and

$$(A^{-1})_{11} \in [.333, .334][1.99, 2.01]$$
$$\subset [.66267, .67134] \subset [.662, .672]$$

(to three figures).

As a second example, consider the interval matrix

$$M = \begin{pmatrix} [.999, 1.01] & [-1.00 \cdot 10^{-3}, 1.00 \cdot 10^{-3}] \\ [-1.00 \cdot 10^{-3}, 1.00 \cdot 10^{-3}] & [.999, 1.01] \end{pmatrix} \tag{5-10}$$

The interval matrix whose elements are the actual ranges of values of elements of the inverse of a real matrix with elements chosen independently from the corresponding elements of M can be determined from equations (5–4), (5–5), (5–6), (5–7) to satisfy the following:
$A_{\mathrm{real}} \subset M$ implies that

$$A^{-1} \subset \begin{pmatrix} \cdots & \cdots \\ \cdots & [.990098, 1.001003] \end{pmatrix} \tag{5-11}$$

PROBLEM 5.3. Determine bounds on the three other elements of A^{-1} in (5–11).

Using three-significant-figure rounded-interval arithmetic and the formulas (5–4), (5–5), (5–6), (5–7), we obtain for the inverses of real matrices $A \subset M$, the bounds

$$A^{-1} \subset \begin{pmatrix} \cdots & \cdots \\ \cdots & [.960, 1.02] \end{pmatrix} \tag{5-12}$$

PROBLEM 5.4. Compute the three other elements of the matrix in (5–12) by using three-figure rounded-interval arithmetic in (5–5), (5–6), and (5–7).

In the next section we will describe a method found by E. Hansen which combines the use of interval arithmetic, ordinary machine arithmetic, and power-series expansion of matrices to obtain sharper bounds on the elements of an inverse matrix than are possible for interval matrices using straightforward interval-arithmetic evaluation of the formulas for direct matrix inversion.

5.2 THE METHOD OF E. HANSEN

Even if we evaluate formula (5–4) with exact (i.e., infinite-precision) interval arithmetic, the resulting interval for $(A^{-1})_{22}$ in (5–12) is still wider than the sharper bound in (5–11); in fact, we obtain

$$(A^{-1})_{22} \subset [.9793\ldots, 1.0120\ldots]$$

upon substituting the elements of the matrix M given by (5-10) into equation (5-4) and using *exact* interval arithmetic for the evaluation of the resulting interval expression. The reason for this is the multiple occurrence of the variable a_{11}.

Of course by performing an a priori analysis of the propagation of initial and rounding errors for a given formula (see [5], [7], and [8]) it will often be *possible* to obtain much sharper bounds than those provided by straightforward use of interval arithmetic alone. On the other hand it may be a very laborious task to actually do so [7]. Our approach is to seek means of enabling the computer to do the work of obtaining error bounds for its own computations.

It is sometimes possible, for a given class of computational problems, to find an algorithm for which a priori error estimates can be combined with some use of interval arithmetic in the evaluation of the algorithm in order to obtain an augmented algorithm for the machine computation of rigorous and usefully sharp upper and lower bounds to the exact solution.

Hansen's method does this for matrix inversion with what amounts to an interval version of a well-known method in matrix theory [6].

Suppose A is an n-by-n interval matrix. Let A_r be a real matrix with machine numbers chosen from the corresponding elements of A. For example, if $A_{ij} = [a_{ij}, b_{ij}]$, take

$$(A_r)_{ij} = \frac{a_{ij} + b_{ij}}{2}$$

where the averages are computed with unrounded, *s*ingle-precision, *f*loating-*p*oint machine arithmetic. We require only that $(A_r)_{ij} \in A_{ij}$.

Now compute an approximate inverse B to A_r using s.p., f.p. machine arithmetic with some matrix-inversion algorithm.

Define E by

$$E = I - AB \qquad (5\text{-}13)$$

(I is the identity) where the arithmetic operations are to be carried out in *double-precision rounded-interval arithmetic and the results rounded to a single-precision interval matrix E.*

We define a norm for an interval matrix A by

$$\|A\| = \max_{1 \le i \le n} \sum_{j=1}^{n} \max \left(|a_{ij}|, |b_{ij}| \right) \qquad (5\text{-}14)$$

Notice that $\|A\|$ is an upper bound to the "maximum row sum" norm of any real matrix $A_r \subset A$. That is,

$$\|A\| \ge \|A_r\| = \max_{1 \le i \le n} \sum_{j=1}^{n} |(A_r)_{ij}| \qquad \text{for } A_r \subset A$$

Now if $\|E\| < 1$, then for any real matrix $E_r \subset E$ we have the power-series representation

$$(I - E_r)^{-1} = I + E_r + E_r^2 + \cdots$$

Put another way, from the "multiplicative property" of the norm we have

$$\|E_r^m\| \leq \|E_r\|^m$$

and from

$$\|E_r\| \leq \|E\| < 1$$

we have

$$\|E_r^m\| \leq \|E\|^m \to 0 \qquad \text{as } m \to \infty$$

Now call $I + E_r + \cdots + E_r^m = S_r^{(m)}$; then

$$(I - E_r)S_r^{(m)} = I - E_r^{m+1} \tag{5-15}$$

and

$$\|I - (I - E_r)S_r^{(m)}\| \to 0 \qquad \text{as } m \to \infty$$

Since the norm of the difference converges to 0, then each element of $S_r^{(m)}$ converges to the corresponding element of $(I - E_r)^{-1}$. Furthermore, we have

$$\|(I - E_r)^{-1}\| \leq 1 + \|E\| + \|E\|^2 + \cdots \leq \frac{1}{1 - \|E\|}$$

and from (5-15), $(I - E_r)^{-1} - S_r^{(m)} = E_r^{m+1}(I - E_r)^{-1}$, so

$$\|(I - E_r)^{-1} - S_r^{(m)}\| \leq \frac{\|E\|^{m+1}}{1 - \|E\|} \tag{5-16}$$

From the definition of E in equation (5–13) we see that for any real matrix $A_r \subset A$, the matrix $E_r = I - A_r B$ is contained in E and therefore satisfies (5–16) and also

$$(I - E_r)^{-1} = (A_r B)^{-1} = B^{-1}A_r^{-1}$$

or

$$A_r^{-1} = B(I - E_r)^{-1} \tag{5-17}$$

Let $P^{(m)}$ be an n-by-n interval matrix with identical elements, each of which is the interval

$$\left[\frac{-\|E\|^{m+1}}{1 - \|E\|}, \frac{\|E\|^{m+1}}{1 - \|E\|} \right]$$

From (5–16) and (5–17), it follows that every real matrix $A_r \subset A$ satisfies

$$A_r^{-1} \subset B(S_r^{(m)} + P^{(m)}) \tag{5-18}$$

where the arithmetic operations in (5–18) are exact-interval arithmetic.

We define an interval matrix $S^{(m)}$ by

$$S^{(m)} = ((E + I)E + I)E + \cdots + I \qquad (m \text{ sums}) \tag{5-19}$$

(by which we mean the nested form of the expression $I + E + E^2 + \cdots + E^m$). From (5–18), it follows that for *any* $A_r \subset A$, we have

$$A_r^{-1} \subset B(S^{(m)} + P^{(m)}) \tag{5–20}$$

In (5–20), we suppose that from (5–13) and (5–14) we have computed a machine single-precision upper bound ρ to $\|E\|^{m+1}/(1 - \|E\|)$ and have formed the matrix $P^{(m)}$ with elements $[-\rho, \rho]$.

For the evaluation of (5–20): Compute

$$S^{(m)} - I = (\cdots(E + I)E + \cdots + I)E$$

in single-precision (rounded) interval arithmetic; add $P^{(m)}$ in *single precision* *interval* *arithmetic*; compute $B(S^{(m)} - I + P^{(m)})$ in s.p.i.a.; finally, add B to this in double-precision (rounded) interval arithmetic.

While there are still a number of details left to be considered, particularly the choice of m, the number of terms in the series for $(I - E)^{-1}$, we will illustrate the steps of the procedure at this point by applying the method of Hansen to the numerical example (5–10) discussed in the previous section.

For this, we will suppose for the purpose of comparison with previous bounds that three-figure decimal arithmetic is single-precision.

(1) Our matrix A is

$$A = \begin{pmatrix} [.999, 1.01] & [-1.00 \cdot 10^{-3}, 1.00 \cdot 10^{-3}] \\ [-1.00 \cdot 10^{-3}, 1.00 \cdot 10^{-3}] & [.999, 1.01] \end{pmatrix}$$

(2) From A we select the real matrix (by averaging endpoints with three-figure unrounded arithmetic).

$$A_r = \begin{pmatrix} 1 & 0 \\ 0 & 1 \end{pmatrix}$$

(3) Next, we obtain an approximate inverse B for A_r; in this case we will suppose that

$$B = \begin{pmatrix} 1 & 0 \\ 0 & 1 \end{pmatrix} = I$$

(4) We compute E by (5–13):

$$E = I - AB = I - AI = I - A$$

$$= \begin{pmatrix} 1 & 0 \\ 0 & 1 \end{pmatrix} - \begin{pmatrix} [.999, 1.01] & [-10^{-3}, 10^{-3}] \\ [-10^{-3}, 10^{-3}] & [.999, 1.01] \end{pmatrix}$$

$$= \begin{pmatrix} [-.01, .001] & [-.001, .001] \\ [-.001, .001] & [-.01, .001] \end{pmatrix}$$

(5) Next, we obtain $\|E\|$ using (5–14):

$$\|E\| = .011$$

$$1 - \|E\| = .989$$

$$\frac{\|E\|^{m+1}}{1 - \|E\|} = \frac{(.011)^{m+1}}{.989}$$

We will consider two cases: $m = 1, m = 2$.

(a) *for* $m = 1$, we can put

$$\rho = \rho_1 = .000123 > \frac{(.011)^2}{.989}$$

(b) *for* $m = 2$, we can put

$$\rho = \rho_2 = .135 \cdot 10^{-5} > \frac{(.011)^3}{.989}$$

(6) For these two cases, the bounds given by (5–20) become

(a) *with* $m = 1$: for every $A_r \subset A$,

$$A_r^{-1} \subset B(E + P^{(1)}) + \text{d.p. } B$$

where

$$P^{(1)} = \begin{pmatrix} [-.000123, .000123] & [-.000123, .000123] \\ [-.000123, .000123] & [-.000123, .000123] \end{pmatrix} \quad \text{and} \quad B = I$$

so we get

$$A_r^{-1} \subset \begin{pmatrix} [-.0102, .00113] & [-.00113, .00113] \\ [-.00113, .00113] & [-.0102, .00113] \end{pmatrix} + \text{d.p. } I$$

or

$$A_r^{-1} \subset \begin{pmatrix} [.9898, 1.00113] & [-.00113, .00113] \\ [-.00113, .00113] & [.9898, 1.00113] \end{pmatrix} \tag{5-21}$$

Compare this with (1) the actual range of values (to six places) (5–11), (2) the rounded-interval arithmetic bounds (5–12), and (3) the exact-interval arithmetic bounds mentioned at the beginning of this section.

(b) *with* $m = 2$: for every $A_r \subset A$,

$$A_r^{-1} \subset B(E(I + E) + P^{(2)}) + \text{d.p. } B$$

where $B = I$ and

$$P^{(2)} = \begin{pmatrix} [-.135 \cdot 10^{-5}, .135 \cdot 10^{-5}] & [-.135 \cdot 10^{-5}, .135 \cdot 10^{-5}] \\ [-.135 \cdot 10^{-5}, .135 \cdot 10^{-5}] & [-.135 \cdot 10^{-5}, .135 \cdot 10^{-5}] \end{pmatrix}$$

We compute, to three figures,

$$I + E = \begin{pmatrix} [.99, 1.01] & [-.001, .001] \\ [-.001, .001] & [.99, 1.01] \end{pmatrix}$$

$$E(I + E) = \begin{pmatrix} [-.0102, .00102] & [-.00102, .00102] \\ [-.00102, .00102] & [-.0102, .00102] \end{pmatrix}$$

$$E(I + E) + P^{(2)} = \begin{pmatrix} [-.0103, .00103] & [-.00103, .00103] \\ [-.00103, .00103] & [-.0103, .00103] \end{pmatrix}$$

Adding $B = I$, to six figures, we get

$$A_r^{-1} \subset \begin{pmatrix} [.9897, 1.00103] & [-.00103, .00103] \\ [-.00103, .00103] & [.9897, 1.00103] \end{pmatrix}$$

By going to high enough (multiple) precision in the computation of the endpoints of the rounded-interval arithmetic results and by taking enough terms in the series for $(I - E)^{-1}$ in order to make $P^{(m)}$ correspondingly small, we can use Hansen's method to compute *on the machine* upper and lower bounds close to the actual range of values of A_r^{-1} for $A_r \subset A$, if $w(A) = \max\limits_{i,j} w(A_{ij})$ is small. From equation (5–13) we have

$$E = I - \{A_r | A_r \subset A\}B$$

Define $E_r = I - A_r B$ (real arithmetic). Thus

$$A_r^{-1} = B(I - E_r)^{-1}$$

and the formula (5–20) bounds the set of real matrices A_r^{-1} for $A_r \subset A$, by

$$\{A_r^{-1} | A_r \subset A\} \subset B(S^{(m)} + P^{(m)}) \qquad (5\text{–}22)$$

The matrix $P^{(m)}$ has all elements identically the same; if $w(A)$ $\equiv \max\limits_{i,j} \{w(A_{ij})\}$ is small enough and if B is a good enough approximation to some A_r^{-1}, then $\|E\|$ will, in fact be less than 1 and, by taking m large enough, the elements $[-\rho, \rho]$ of $P^{(m)}$ can be taken arbitrarily "small," i.e., ρ can be taken arbitrarily small. With high enough machine precision, the right-hand side of (5–22) can be evaluated arbitrarily close to its exact-interval arithmetic value.

The question of how close to $\{A_r^{-1} | A_r \subset A\}$ the bounds given by Hansen's method can be made by going to high enough machine precision in the rounded-interval arithmetic involves a comparison for arbitrary positive integers m of the interval matrices

$$S^{(m)} = I + E(I + E(I + \cdots + E(I + E)\cdots) \qquad (m \text{ sums})$$

and

$$S_m = \{I + E_r + E_r^2 + \cdots + E_r^m | E_r = I - A_r B, A_r \subset A\}$$

For $m = 1$, we have

$$S^{(1)} = I + E$$

and

$$S_1 = \{I + E_r | E_r = I - A_r B, A_r \subset A\}$$
$$= S^{(1)}$$

because of the single occurrence of the elements A_{ij} in $E = I - AB$. Thus, $E = \{E_r | A_r \subset A\}$.

For $m > 1$, we wish to compare the widths of the elements of $S^{(m)}$ with those of S_m. Since $(S^{(m)})_{ij} \supset (S_m)_{ij}$ for all i, j, it follows from Lemma 4.2 that

$$w((S^{(m)})_{ij}) \leq w((S_m)_{ij}) + 2d((S^{(m)})_{ij}, (S_m)_{ij}) \tag{5-23}$$

From Lemma 4.1 it follows that the distance $d((S^{(m)})_{ij}, (S_m)_{ij})$ will be less than $\epsilon > 0$, provided that for every $x \in (S^{(m)})_{ij}$ there is a $y \in (S_m)_{ij}$ such that $|x - y| < \epsilon$. [For intervals $I \subset J$, condition (1) in Lemma 4.1 is automatically satisfied.]

If $x \in (S^{(m)})_{ij}$, then x is the ijth element of a matrix of the form

$$M_1 = I + E_{r_1} + E_{r_1}E_{r_2} + \cdots + E_{r_1}E_{r_2}\ldots E_{r_m} \tag{5-24}$$

where $E_{r_p} \in E$ is a real matrix for $p = 1, 2, \ldots, m$. Choose y to be the corresponding ijth element of the matrix $M_2 = I + E_{r_1} + E_{r_1}^2 + \cdots + E_{r_1}^m$ for the same E_{r_1} as in (5-24). Then we have

$$M_1 - M_2 = E_{r_1}\{(E_{r_2} - E_{r_1}) + (E_{r_2}E_{r_3} - E_{r_1}^2) + \cdots$$
$$+ (E_{r_2}E_{r_3}\ldots E_{r_m} - E_{r_1}^{m-1})\}$$

Since $\|E_{r_p}\| \leq \|E\|$, it follows that

$$\|M_1 - M_2\| \leq \|E\|\{2\|E\| + 2\|E^2\| + \cdots + 2\|E\|^{m-1}\}$$

and therefore we have

$$|x - y| \leq \|M_1 - M_2\| \leq 2\|E\|^2(1 + \|E\| + \cdots + \|E\|^{m-2})$$

and, for $\|E\| < 1$,

$$|x - y| \leq \frac{2\|E\|^2}{1 - \|E\|}$$

Notice that, in the special case $m = 2$, we have $|x - y| \leq 2\|E\|^2$. In any case, from (5-23) we conclude that for arbitrary $m > 1$,

$$w((S^{(m)})_{ij}) \leq w((S_m)_{ij}) + 4\frac{\|E\|^2}{1 - \|E\|}$$

Furthermore, since for some $A_r \subset A$, we have $B = A_r^{-1} + Q$, where Q has arbitrarily small elements for high enough machine precision in the computation of B, we can write $A = A_r + D$ for an interval matrix D with $D_{ij} \in [-w(A), w(A)]$; then $E = I - (A_r + D)(A_r^{-1} + Q)$ and so $E \subset -A_rQ - DB$. Therefore

$$\|E\| \leq \|A\|\,\|Q\| + nw(A)\|B\|$$

The inequalities we have written can be put together to obtain the result that for high eough machine precision, say, so that

$$\|Q\| \leq \frac{w(A)\|B\|}{\|A\|}$$

we have

$$w(S^{(m)}) \leq w(S_m) + \frac{4((n+1)w(A)\|B\|)^2}{1 - (n+1)w(A)\|B\|} \qquad (5\text{-}25)$$

provided that

$$w(A) < \frac{1}{(n+1)\|B\|}$$

If ρ is also chosen less than the second term on the right-hand side of (5-25), then, because of $S_m \subset S^{(m)}$ and (5-25) and (5-22) we can write

$$B(S^{(m)} + P^{(m)}) = \{A_r^{-1} | A_r \subset A\} + H$$

for an interval matrix H whose elements H_{ij} satisfy, for all $i, j = 1, 2, \ldots, m$,

$$|H_{i,j}| \leq \frac{8(n+1)^2 \|B\|^3}{1 - (n+1)w(A)\|B\|} (w(A))^2 \qquad (5\text{-}26)$$

We can interpret (5-26) as saying that the upper and lower bounds given by Hansen's method to any component of the interval matrix $\{A_r^{-1} | A_r \subset A\}$ fail to be sharp by a quantity of order the square of the width of A, given high enough machine precision in the computations.

Clearly the appropriate choice for m in (5-20) depends on the machine precision to be used in the rounded-interval arithmetic and on the size of $\|E\|$ and should probably be made so that ρ is about as small as a low-order bit in, say, the largest element of E, or perhaps $\rho = $ low-order bit in $\|E\|$ would be reasonable, relative to the precision used.

*PROBLEM 5.5. Write a program for inverting interval matrices based on Hansen's method.

REFERENCES

1. DWYER, P.S., *Linear Computations*. New York: John Wiley & Sons, Inc., 1951.
2. DWYER, P.S., "Matrix inversion with the square root method," *Technometrics*, 6: 2 (1964), 197-213.
3. FADDEEVA, V.N., *Computational Methods of Linear Algebra*. New York: Dover, Publications, Inc., 1959.
4. HANSEN, E., "Interval arithmetic in matrix computation," *J.S.I.A.M.*, series B, *Numerical Analysis*, part I, 2: 2(1965), 308-320.
5. HOUSEHOLDER, A.S., *Principles of Numerical Analysis*. New York: McGraw-Hill Book Company, 1953.
6. HOUSEHOLDER, A.S., *The Theory of Matrices in Numerical Analysis* (esp. p. 95). New York: Blaisdell Publishing Co., 1964.
7. VON NEUMANN, J., and GOLDSTINE, H., "Numerical inverting of matrices of high order," *Bull. Amer. Math. Soc.*, 53 (1947), 1021-1099.
8. WILKINSON, J.H., *Rounding Errors in Algebraic Processes*. Englewood Cliffs, N. J.: Prentice-Hall, Inc., 1963.

6 VALUES AND RANGES OF VALUES OF REAL FUNCTIONS

6.1 INTRODUCTION

Computations in finite-precision or rounded-interval arithmetic by the computer yield upper and lower bounds to exact values and ranges of values of real rational functions. By examples in the previous chapters we have shown that these machine-computed bounds do not usually converge to the range of values of a real rational function as the precision (of the machine arithmetic used) increases. Such convergence holds, generally speaking, only for the case of exact initial data.

The computation of ranges of values of real *rational* functions is of particular importance for two reasons. First, each finite sequence of arithmetic operations in a computer program defines a *rational* function whose values are computed (approximately) by executing that part of the program, and for *initial data* that are *inexact* we wish to know the range of possible values of such rational functions. Second, we wish to be able to bound programmed expressions for *remainder terms* in the truncation of infinite series. A remainder term can often be expressed in terms of a variable ξ whose value is only known to lie within a certain interval $a \leq \xi \leq b$.

In Section 5.2 we have seen the combination of a truncated series expansion with a machine-computable expression bounding the remainder together with interval arithmetic evaluation of an algorithm produce narrower bounding intervals for the matrix-inversion problem than are possible using interval arithmetic alone.

In Chapter 4 we gave a procedure involving unions of n intervals which does, in fact, converge to the range of values of a real rational function as

n increases. However, the convergence is too slow for the procedure to be of much practical value, even with microsecond multiplication times.

In this chapter we collect together some practical devices for improving the bounds on the ranges of values of real rational functions given by straightforward interval-arithmetic evaluation. We consider also the machine computation of upper and lower bounds to values and· ranges of values of *irrational* real functions.

If X_1 and X_2 are intervals containing an interval I, then the *intersection* of X_1 and X_2 also contains I. In symbols, $I \subset X_1$, $I \subset X_2$ implies $I \subset X_1 \cap X_2$. Thus if X_1 and X_2 are machine-computed bounding (containing) intervals for I, we may get a narrower machine-computed bound by taking the intersection $X_1 \cap X_2$.

Cancellation or *reduction of the number of occurrences of a variable* before interval evaluation can reduce interval widths. For example, in Chapter 5 we gave an example in which by rewriting the expression $a_{22}/(a_{22} - 2)$ as

$$\frac{a_{22}}{a_{22} - 2} = \frac{a_{22} - 2}{a_{22} - 2} + \frac{2}{a_{22} - 1} = 1 + \frac{2}{a_{22} - 2}$$

the resulting expression had fewer occurrences of the variable a_{22} (in fact, only one); and substitution of an interval of values for a_{22} in the resulting expression yielded a narrower interval (in fact, the exact range of values) than that obtained from the original expression. As another example, the expression $X - X$ produces the value 0 for every real number X and the degenerate interval 0 has width zero, whereas substituting an interval of values in the expression $X - X$ produces, for example,

$$[0, 1] - [0, 1] = [-1, 1], \quad \text{using interval subtraction.}$$

Use of *subdistributivity*, (3-4), can reduce interval widths. For example, the "nested" form of a polynomial gives intervals contained in and often narrower than those produced using the sum of powers, i.e., for intervals

$$A_0, A_1, \ldots, A_n, X$$

we have

$$(\cdots((A_n)X + A_{n-1})X + \cdots A_1)X + A_0$$
$$\subset A_n X \cdot X \cdots X + \cdots + A_2 \cdot X \cdot X + A_1 \cdot X + A_0$$

For a given real rational expression there are infinitely many other expressions which define the same real rational function ; e.g.,

$$x(1 - x) = x - x^2 = -6 + (x + 2)(5 - (x + 2)) = \cdots$$

For a given interval $[a, b]$ there may be one of these expressions which produces a narrower interval than the originally given expression. In Section 6.2 we will give a scheme for selecting a particular rational interval expression which is, at least, a candidate for a "canonical form." Each equivalent real expression gives rise to a (usually) distinct rational interval function, e.g., $X - X \cdot X$ and $X(1 - X)$ do not produce the same interval results for an arbitrary choice of the interval X. Indeed,

$$[0, 1] - [0, 1] \cdot [0, 1] = [0, 1] - [0, 1] = [-1, 1]$$

whereas

$$[0, 1](1 - [0, 1]) = [0, 1]([0, 1]) = [0, 1]$$

6.2 THE CENTERED FORM

There is a particular way of selecting a rational interval expression $F(X_1, X_2, \ldots, X_n)$ given a real rational expression $f(x_1, x_2, \ldots, x_n)$ and a particular set of interval numbers over which the real variables range which in many cases gives a narrower interval containing the range of values of f, i.e.,

$$\bar{f}(X_1, X_2, \ldots, X_n) = \{f(x_1, x_2, \ldots, x_n) | x_i \in X_i, i = 1, 2, \ldots, n\}$$

than the interval expression directly corresponding to $f(x_1, x_2, \ldots, x_n)$. It is what we might call the *centered* form. An example will illustrate the idea.

Given $f(x) = x - x^2$, and an interval $[a, b]$, we first write $y = x - (a + b)/2$ then substitute $y + (a + b)/2$ for x in the expression $f(x)$ to obtain

$$f(x) = \left(y + \frac{a + b}{2}\right) - \left(y + \frac{a + b}{2}\right)^2$$

Then we rewrite this expression in nested form relative to y, obtaining

$$f(x) = \frac{a + b}{2} - \left(\frac{a + b}{2}\right)^2 + y((1 - (a + b)) - y)$$

or, replacing y by $x - (a + b)/2$, we obtain

$$f(x) = \frac{a + b}{2} - \left(\frac{a + b}{2}\right)^2 + \left(x - \left(\frac{a + b}{2}\right)\right)$$
$$\times \left((1 - (a + b)) - \left(x - \left(\frac{a + b}{2}\right)\right)\right)$$

Now we define the rational interval function

$$F(X) = \frac{a + b}{2} - \left(\frac{a + b}{2}\right)^2 + \left(X - \left(\frac{a + b}{2}\right)\right)$$
$$\times \left((1 - (a + b)) - \left(X - \left(\frac{a + b}{2}\right)\right)\right)$$

We will still have $\{f(x) | a \le x \le b\} \subset F([a, b])$ and, putting $X = [a, b]$, we obtain, if $c = (a + b)/2$ and $r = (b - a)/2$,

$$F([a, b]) = c(1 - c) - [-r, r](1 - 2c + [-r, r]) \qquad (6\text{-}1)$$

The representation (6-1) shows the computation of an interval $F([a, b])$ containing $\{x - x^2 | x \in [a, b]\}$ in terms of the value of $x - x^2$ at the center (or "midpoint"), c, of $[a, b]$ plus an interval-arithmetic computation which produces intervals of narrow width if the width of $[a, b]$ is narrow (i.e., small).

In particular, if $c = \frac{1}{2}$, we have from (6-1), for $X = [a, b]$, $F(X) = \frac{1}{4} - (X - \frac{1}{2})^2$,

$$F\left(\frac{1}{2} + [-r, r]\right) = \frac{1}{4} + [-r^2, r^2] = \left[\frac{1}{4} - r^2, \frac{1}{4} + r^2\right] \qquad (6\text{-}2)$$

Compare (6-2) with the actual range of values of f for $x \in [\frac{1}{2} - r, \frac{1}{2} + r]$, namely

$$\left\{f(x) = x - x^2 | \frac{1}{2} - r \leq x \leq \frac{1}{2} + r\right\} = \left[\frac{1}{4} - r^2, \frac{1}{4}\right] \qquad (6\text{-}3)$$

and with the interval computed from interval-arithmetic evaluation of the nested form of $f(x) = x - x^2$, namely $X(1 - X)$ or

$$\left[\frac{1}{2} - r, \frac{1}{2} + r\right]\left(1 - \left[\frac{1}{2} - r, \frac{1}{2} + r\right]\right)$$

$$= \left[\frac{1}{2} - r, \frac{1}{2} + r\right]\left[\frac{1}{2} - r, \frac{1}{2} + r\right] \qquad (6\text{-}4)$$

$$= \begin{cases} \left[\left(\frac{1}{2} - r\right)^2, \left(\frac{1}{2} + r\right)^2\right] & \text{if } r \leq \frac{1}{2} \\ \left[\left(\frac{1}{2} - r\right)\left(\frac{1}{2} + r\right), \left(\frac{1}{2} + r\right)^2\right] & \text{if } r > \frac{1}{2} \end{cases}$$

In summary of these results :

(1) The upper bound (or right endpoint) given by the *nested form* $F(X) = X(1 - X)$ is: $(\frac{1}{2} + r)^2 = \frac{1}{4} + r + r^2$.

(2) The upper bound given by the *centered form* $F(X) = \frac{1}{4} - (X - \frac{1}{2})^2$ is: $\frac{1}{4} + r^2$.

(3) The *actual* upper bound to $\{x - x^2 | \frac{1}{2} - r \leq x \leq \frac{1}{2} + r\}$ is, of course: $\frac{1}{4}$.

For the same real expression $f(x) = x - x^2$ and an interval $X = [a, b]$ with $c = (a + b)/2 = \frac{1}{4}$, we have for $r \leq \frac{1}{4}$, from (6-1), the centered form

$$F(X) = \frac{3}{16} - \left(X - \frac{1}{4}\right)\left(\frac{1}{2} - \left(X - \frac{1}{4}\right)\right) = \frac{3}{16} - \left(X - \frac{1}{4}\right)\left(\frac{3}{4} - X\right)$$

or

$$F\left(\frac{1}{4} + [-r, r]\right) = \frac{3}{16} - [-r, r]\left(\frac{1}{2} + [-r, r]\right)$$

$$= \left[\frac{3}{16} - \frac{r}{2} - r^2, \frac{3}{16} + \frac{r}{2} + r^2 \right]$$

The actual range of values, $f(x) = \{x - x^2 | x \in \frac{1}{4} + [-r, r]\}$ for $r \le \frac{1}{4}$, is

$$\left[\frac{3}{16} - \frac{r}{2} - r^2, \frac{3}{16} + \frac{r}{2} - r^2 \right]$$

The nested form (of $x - x^2$), $F(X) = X(1 - X)$, gives (for $r \le \frac{1}{4}$)

$$\left(\frac{1}{4} + [-r, r] \right) \left(-\left(\frac{1}{4} + [-r, r] \right) \right) = \left[\frac{3}{16} - r - r^2, \frac{3}{16} + r + r^2 \right]$$

From these computations we see that a *centered* form *may* give better bounds than a more straightforward interval version of the given form.

Given any real rational expression $f(x_1, x_2, \ldots, x_n)$ and any vector of real numbers $c = (c_1, c_2, \ldots, c_n)$ at which the value of f is defined (i.e., not at a singularity of f), we can write f as

$$f(x_1, x_2, \ldots, x_n) = f(c_1, c_2, \ldots, c_n) + g(x_1 - c_1, \ldots, x_n - c_n) \quad (6\text{-}5)$$

by substituting $x_i = c_i + y_i, i = 1, 2, \ldots, n$ into the expression for $f(x_1, \ldots, x_n)$, and forming

$$g(x_1 - c_1, \ldots, x_n - c_n) = g(y_1, \ldots, y_n)$$
$$= f(y_1 + c_1, \ldots, y_n + c_n) - f(c_1, \ldots, c_n) \quad (6\text{-}6)$$

We will suppose that the expression for $g(y_1, \ldots, y_n)$ is arranged in one of a number of equivalent ways so that the number of occurrences of the variables $y_1, y_2, \ldots, y_n$ in the expression chosen for $g(y_1, \ldots, y_n)$ cannot be further reduced by cancellations; e.g.,

$$g(y_1, y_2) = (y_1 + y_2)(y_1 - y_2) \quad \textit{or} \quad g(y_1, y_2) = y_1^2 - y_2^2$$

but *not*

$$g(y_1, y_2) = 2y_1^2 - y_2^2 - y_1^2$$

Using (6-6) to form the expression for g in (6-5), we can substitute interval variables $Y_1, Y_2, \ldots, Y_n$ for the real variables $y_1, \ldots, y_n$ occurring in the expression for $g(y_1, \ldots, y_n)$ and obtain an expression we can denote by $g(Y_1, Y_2, \ldots, Y_n)$; interpreting the arithmetic operations as interval arithmetic operations, the resulting expression $g(Y_1, Y_2, \ldots, Y_n)$ is a rational interval expression.

Denote the midpoint of an interval $[a, b]$ by

$$m([a, b]) = \frac{a + b}{2}$$

We form the expression

$$F(X_1, X_2, \ldots, X_n) = f(m(X_1), m(X_2), \ldots, m(X_n))$$
$$+ g(X_1 - m(X_1), \ldots, X_n - m(X_n)) \quad (6\text{-}7)$$

corresponding to (6-5) by substituting $X_i - m(X_i)$ for Y_i in the rational interval expression $g(Y_1, Y_2, \ldots, Y_n)$.

The equation (6-7), then, gives a centered form of a rational interval expression with real restriction $f(x_1, x_2, \ldots, x_n)$.

For an interval vector X of zero width (i.e., $X = (X_1, X_2, \ldots, X_n)$, $w(X) = \max_i w(X_i) = 0, i = 1, 2, \ldots, n$) we have $X_i = m(X_i)$, and, from (6-5), $g(0, 0, \ldots, 0) = 0$, so that

$$F(m(X_1), \ldots, m(X_n)) = f(m(X_1), \ldots, m(X_n))$$

It follows from Theorem 4.3 that g in equation (6-7) is continuous for $X_1 \subset A_1, X_2 \subset A_2, \ldots, X_n \subset A_n$ such that $F(A_1, A_2, \ldots, A_n)$ in (6-7) is defined (is an interval). Therefore $|g(X_1 - m(X_1), \ldots, X_n - m(X_n))|$ is small for intervals $X_1, \ldots, X_n$ of small width.

Of course, we have for the centered form of F in (6-7) the inclusion property

$$\bar{f}(X_1, \ldots, X_n) \subset F(X_1, \ldots, X_n)$$

where $\bar{f}$ is the united extension of f.

Based on the numerical examples above for $f(x) = x - x^2$ and others* we have tried, and also considering (5-26), we make the following conjecture: with F given by (6-7) we have

$$w(F(X_1, \ldots, X_n)) \leq w(\bar{f}(X_1, \ldots, X_n)) + O(w(X)^2)$$

The discussion of this section on the "centered form" is admittedly rather imprecise. In particular the "*definition*" of the centered form was rather vague. Hopefully a more precise and elegant presentation of the notion will be found. In fact, there is the possibility of the determination of *a* centered form *by the computer*, given an expression $f(x_1, x_2, \ldots, x_n)$ *and* a real vector $(c_1, c_2, \ldots, c_n)$, say $c_i = m(X_i)$, for some interval vector $X_1, X_2, \ldots, X_n$ for which $\bar{f}(X_1, X_2, \ldots, X_n)$ is desired. This would require a computer program capable of algebraic manipulations.

For the moment, we will be content to indicate further the desirability of such results by giving another numerical example using the notion of the centered form.

In problem 5.1 we asked for the computation of (in slightly different notation)

$$\bar{f}(X_1, X_2) \qquad \text{for } f(x_1, x_2) = \frac{x_1 + x_2}{x_1 - x_2}$$

with $X_1 = [1, 2]$ and $X_2 = [5, 10]$. We also asked for $(X_1 + X_2)/(X_1 - X_2)$

---

*Mr. Augustine S. Chai has pointed out that for the range of values of $f(x) = x + x^2$ for $x \in X = [2 - \epsilon, 2 + \epsilon]$ the nested and sum-of-powers forms give *exact* results for $\epsilon \leq 2$ whereas the centered form gives a lower bound that is $2\epsilon^2$ less than the actual lower bound to $\bar{f}(X)$.

in interval arithmetic. The answers are

$$\bar{f}([1, 2], [5, 10]) = \left[-\frac{7}{3}, -\frac{11}{9}\right]$$

$$\frac{[1, 2] + [5, 10]}{[1, 2] - [5, 10]} = \left[-4, -\frac{2}{3}\right]$$

To obtain the centered form, write

$$\frac{x_2 + x_1}{x_1 - x_2} = \frac{c_1 + c_2}{c_1 - c_2} + g(x_1 - c_1, x_2 - c_2)$$

where $g(x_1 - c_1, x_2 - c_2)$ is obtained by putting $x_1 = c_1 + y_1, x_2 = c_2 + y_2$ and forming

$$g(y_1, y_2) = \frac{c_1 + y_1 + c_2 + y_2}{c_1 + y_1 - (c_2 + y_2)} - \frac{c_1 + c_2}{c_1 - c_2}$$

$$= \frac{2(c_1 y_2 - c_2 y_1)}{(c_1 - c_2)^2 + (c_1 - c_2)(y_1 - y_2)} \tag{6-8}$$

The numerator in (6–8) is obtained by performing elementary algebraic multiplications of the variables and constants and carrying out the cancellations indicated in the following:

$$2(c_1 y_2 - c_2 y_1) = \cancel{c_1^2} + \cancel{c_1 y_1} + \cancel{c_1 c_2} + c_1 y_2 - \cancel{c_2 c_1}$$
$$- c_2 y_1 - \cancel{c_2^2} - \cancel{c_2 y_2} - \cancel{c_1^2} - \cancel{c_1 y_1}$$
$$+ \cancel{c_1 c_2} + c_1 y_2 - \cancel{c_1 c_2} - c_2 y_1 + \cancel{c_2^2}$$
$$+ \cancel{c_2 y_2}$$

There are a number of computer programs under development which promise to enable the computer to carry out such algebraic manipulations.

From (6–8) we obtain the interval expression

$$g(Y_1, Y_2) = \frac{2(c_1 Y_2 - c_2 Y_1)}{(c_1 - c_2)^2 + (c_1 - c_2)(Y_1 - Y_2)}$$

and, finally, the centered form, putting $m(X_1) = c_1, m(X_2) = c_2$, is [from (6–7)]

$$F(X_1, X_2) = \frac{m(X_1) + m(X_2)}{m(X_1) - m(X_2)}$$
$$+ \frac{2(m(X_1)(X_2 - m(X_2)) - m(X_2)(X_1 - m(X_1)))}{(m(X_1) - m(X_2))^2 + (m(X_1) - m(X_2))(X_1 - m(X_1) - X_2 + m(X_2))} \tag{6-9}$$

Now, in (6–9) substitute $X_1 = [1, 2], X_2 = [5, 10], m(X_1) = \frac{3}{2}, m(X_2) = \frac{15}{2}$ and evaluate in interval arithmetic. We obtain in this way

$$F([1, 2], [5, 10]) = -\frac{9}{6} + \frac{2(\frac{3}{2}[-\frac{5}{2}, \frac{5}{2}] - \frac{15}{2}[-\frac{1}{2}, \frac{1}{2}])}{36 + (-6)[-3, 3]}$$

$$= -\frac{9}{6} + \left[-\frac{5}{6}, \frac{5}{6}\right]$$

$$= \left[-\frac{7}{3}, -\frac{2}{3}\right]$$

Thus in this example the centered form gives a sharper bound than the straightforward interval-arithmetic version of the given rational expression.

PROBLEM 6.1 Using the centered form, compute an interval containing $\bar{f}([0, .2])$ in problem 3.6d. Compare this result with (1) the sum-of-powers form and (2) the nested form, using exact-interval arithmetic evaluations, of the polynomial expression given in problem 3.6d.

6.3   THE USE OF THE MEAN-VALUE THEOREM

If f is a real-valued function with a continuous derivative f' on $[a, b]$, in particular, if f is a bounded real rational function on $[a, b]$, then the *mean-value theorem* states that for $x, y \in [a, b]$, we can write

$$f(y) = f(x) + f'(x + \theta(y - x))(y - x)$$

for some $\theta \in [0, 1]$. If $\bar{f}'$ is the united extension of f', then we conclude that

$$f(y) \in f(x) + \bar{f}'(x + (y - x)[0, 1])(y - x)$$

If $F^{(1)}$ is an interval-valued function $F^{(1)}: \mathscr{I}_A \to \mathscr{I}$ defined for $X \subset A$ such that $F^{(1)}(X) \supset \bar{f}'(X)$, then we also have

$$f(y) \in f(x) + F^{(1)}(x + (y - x)[0, 1])(y - x)$$

and also, for $X \subset [a, b] \cap A$,

$$\bar{f}(X) \subset f(x) + F^{(1)}(x + (X - x)[0, 1])(X - x) \tag{6-10}$$

Consider the example $f(x) = x - x^2$ discussed in the beginning of Section 6.2. For $X = [\frac{1}{2} - r, \frac{1}{2} + r]$, we have

exact range of values:

$$\bar{f}(X) = \{f(x) = x - x^2 | x \in X\} = [\frac{1}{4} - r^2, \frac{1}{4}]$$

nested form:

$$\bar{f}(X) \subset X(1 - X) = \begin{cases} [(\frac{1}{2} - r)^2, (\frac{1}{2} + r)^2] & \text{if } r \leq \frac{1}{2} \\ [\frac{1}{4} - r^2, (\frac{1}{2} + r)^2] & \text{if } r > \frac{1}{2} \end{cases}$$

centered form:

$$\bar{f}(X) \subset \frac{1}{4} - (X - \frac{1}{2})^2 = [\frac{1}{4} - r^2, \frac{1}{4} + r^2]$$

and using $F^{(1)}(X) = 1 - 2X$, we have, from (6-10), putting $x = \frac{1}{2}$, the *mean-value form:*

$$\bar{f}(X) \subset \tfrac{1}{4} + (1 - 2(\tfrac{1}{2} + (X - \tfrac{1}{2})\,[0, 1])\,(X - \tfrac{1}{2})$$
$$= [\tfrac{1}{4} - 2r^2, \tfrac{1}{4} + 2r^2]$$

Thus, for small r, in this example the mean-value form gives a result which is better than the nested form, but not as good as the centered form!

On the other hand, the mean-value form does have the advantage that its derivation requires only the determination of an interval expression bounding the derivative of the given expression. In a later chapter we will show how computer programs can be written (and *have*, in fact) which enable the machine to carry out this derivation. In fact, the determination by the machine of expressions (or programs) bounding partial derivatives will also be discussed.

For a real function f of n real variables with continuous partial derivatives $\partial f/\partial x_i, i = 1, 2, \ldots, n$ on an n-dimensional rectangle $B = I_1 \otimes I_2 \otimes \cdots \otimes I_n, I \in \mathscr{I}, i = 1, 2, \ldots, n$ we have the mean-value theorem: for $(x_1, x_2, \ldots, x_n) \in B, (y_1, y_2, \ldots, y_n) \in B$, it follows that

$$f(y_1, y_2, \ldots, y_n) = f(x_1, x_2, \ldots, x_n) + \sum_{j=1}^{n} \frac{\partial f}{\partial x_i}\Big|_{\bar{x}} (y_j - x_j)$$

where $\bar{x}_i = x_i + \theta(y_i - x_i)$ for some $0 \le \theta \le 1$.

For interval functions $F_j \colon \mathscr{I}_{I_1} \otimes \mathscr{I}_{I_2} \otimes \cdots \otimes \mathscr{I}_{I_n} \to \mathscr{I}$ such that

$$F_j(X_1, X_2, \ldots, X_n) \supset \overline{\frac{\partial f}{\partial x_j}}(X_1, \ldots, X_n)$$

with $X_i \subset I_i, i = 1, 2, \ldots, n$, where $\overline{\partial f}/\partial x_j$ is the united extension of $\partial f/\partial x_j$, we have the *mean-value form* given by

$$F(X_1, X_2, \ldots, X_n) = f(x_1, x_2, \ldots, x_n)$$
$$+ \sum_{j=1}^{n} F_j(x_1 + [0, 1]\,(X_1 - x_1), \ldots)\,(X_j - x_j) \qquad (6\text{--}11)$$

with $x_j \in X_j$.

To illustrate (6–11), take our example

$$f(x_1, x_2) = \frac{x_1 + x_2}{x_1 - x_2}$$

discussed in Section 6.2, and for $X_1 = [1, 2], X_2 = [5, 10]$ we can apply (6–11) as follows. First we find that

$$\frac{\partial f}{\partial x_1} = \frac{-2x_2}{(x_1 - x_2)^2}, \qquad \frac{\partial f}{\partial x_2} = \frac{2x_1}{(x_1 - x_2)^2}$$

We choose

$$F_1(X_1, X_2) = \frac{-2X_2}{(X_1 - X_2)(X_1 - X_2)}$$

$$F_2(X_1, X_2) = \frac{2X_1}{(X_1 - X_2)(X_1 - X_2)}$$

Putting $x_1 = \frac{3}{2}, x_2 = \frac{15}{2}$. $X_1 = [1, 2]$, $X_2 = [5, 10]$, we have, from (6–11), by interval-arithmetic computation:

$$F([1, 2], [5, 10]) = \left[\frac{-67}{18}, \frac{13}{18}\right]$$

Compare this with the previous results in Section 6.2.

6.4 DETERMINATION AND USE OF EXTREME VALUES OF RATIONAL FUNCTIONS

A real rational function f without singularities on an interval vector $A = (A_1, A_2, \ldots, A_n)$, $A_i \in \mathscr{I}$, i.e., on an n-dimensional rectangle, assumes its maximum and minimum values at some points, say p and q, in A. The points p and q are not necessarily unique. The determination of a pair of points giving extreme values of f is essentially a "root-finding" problem.

If we determine a small rectangle B, with some sort of interval computation by the machine, which is sure to contain a point p at which f assumes its maximum; then, by interval-arithmetic evaluation of a suitable interval form for f, a reasonably good, even arbitrarily good, upper bound to the maximum value of f can be found. Usually, f will have a certain number of points at which relative maxima and minima occur. The number of *different values of* f at such points, for rational f, *is finite*. Besides these points, f can assume extreme values on the boundary of a rectangular domain. Altogether, a certain finite number of small candidate rectangles can be found by interval root-bounding methods for relative extrema in the interior and on the boundary of A, and together with the corners of A these will constitute a finite set of interval-arithmetic evaluations of f to be carried out in order to determine "global" upper and lower bounds to the range of values of f on A.

In the next chapter we will consider separately the problem of root finding with machine-computed error bounds.

Here we will suppose that such methods are available and consider how to apply them to the problem at hand, that of bounding the range of values of f on A by machine computation.

We consider first a real rational function f of a single real variable x. We wish to determine, as in previous sections of this chapter, an interval-valued function with values $F(X), X \subset A$, such that $F(X) \supset \{f(x)|x \in X\} = \bar{f}(X)$ and such that $F(X)$ is close to $\bar{f}(X)$, i.e., such that $d(F(X), \bar{f}(X))$ is small (see Chapter 4).

The extreme values of f for $x \in A$ will occur at one or more of the following finite number of points: the endpoints of the interval $A = [a, b]$, the roots (zeros), if any, of f' in A, say

$$f'(a_i) = 0, \qquad a_i \in A, \quad i = 1, 2, \ldots, P$$

If we *determine* that f' has *no roots* in A, say we find that $f'(x) > 0$ for all $x \in A$, then we can put

$$F(X) = [f(x_1), f(x_2)] \qquad \text{for } X = [x_1, x_2] \subset A$$

or if $f'(x) < 0$ for all $x \in A$, then we can put

$$F(X) = [f(x_2), f(x_1)] \qquad \text{for } X = [x_1, x_2] \subset A$$

If we do *not* find that f' has no roots in A, we will at least be able to find (with the root-finding methods in the next chapter) a finite set of subintervals $B_1, B_2, \ldots, B_N$ of A ($B_i \subset A$) such that the roots of f' in A, if any, are in the subintervals $B_1, \ldots, B_N$. It may happen that our root-finding methods will not be able to tell for sure that there is *not* a root in a certain interval $B = [b_1, b_2] \subset A$ because of the use of finite-precision rounded-interval arithmetic to bound rounding error in the evaluation of f, f', and the various steps of the root-finding algorithms. No matter, we add the interval B to our collection $B_1, B_2, \ldots, B_N$ anyway. Then we are, at least, certain that the collection of these subintervals does contain *all* the roots of f' in A. By using high enough precision in our rounded-interval arithmetic and iterating the root-finding algorithms enough times, the widths of the intervals $B_1, B_2, \ldots, B_N$ can be made arbitrarily small, provided that the coefficients of f are exactly known real numbers. On the other hand, if the coefficients of f are only known to lie in certain intervals (the case of *inexact initial data*, or perhaps coefficients computed by the machine *with error bounding*), then the widths of the intervals $B_1, B_2, \ldots, B_N$ cannot be made arbitrarily small, because there will be definite intervals of possible values of roots of f'.

Suppose now that we have found a set of intervals $B_1, B_2, \ldots, B_n$ containing the endpoints a, b of $A = [a, b]$ and all the roots of f' which lie in A and that $B_1 < B_2 < \cdots < B_N$. That is, we suppose the intervals are

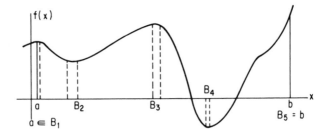

Fig. 6.1

disjoint and, in particular, that $x \in B_i$ implies $x < y$ for all $y \in B_{i+1}$. Figure 6.1 illustrates the sort of configuration we have in mind. The graph of a (supposedly rational) function f is shown over an interval $A = [a, b]$. Disjoint intervals B_1, B_2, B_3, B_4, B_5 are indicated: B_1 contains the left end-points of A and, perhaps, a zero of f'; B_2, B_3, B_4 contain zeros of f'; B_5 consists of the right endpoint of A.

If during the root-finding process a pair of intervals B_i, B_{i+1} happen to be determined which intersect, then we can add their union to the set of disjoint intervals.

After the determination of the intervals $B_1, B_2, \ldots, B_N$ we have the interval A subdivided into the subintervals $B_1, B_2, \ldots, B_N$ and $C_1, C_2, \ldots, C_{N-1}$, where, if $B_i = [a_i, b_i]$, then $C_i = [b_i, a_{i+1}], i = 1, 2, \ldots, N - 1$ and on the intervals C_i the function f is known to be monotonic. Either $f'(x) > 0$ for $x \in C_i$, or $f'(x) < 0$ for $x \in C_i$.

Given an interval $X \subset A$, we write $X = [x_1, x_2]$ as

$$X = (X \cap B_1) \cup (X \cap C_1) \cup \cdots \cup (X \cap C_{N-1}) \cup (X \cap B_N) \quad (6\text{-}12)$$

Either $x_1 \in B_i$ or $x_1 \in C_i$, for some i, and $x_2 \in B_i$ or $x_2 \in C_i$ for some i, with $x_2 \geq x_1$.

In (6-12) a certain number of the leading terms and some of the terms at the end may be empty so that X can be written as, for example,

$$X = [x_1, b_i] \cup C_i \cup B_{i+1} \cup \cdots \cup B_j \cup [b_j, x_2]$$

where

$$x_1 \in B_i = [a_i, b_i] \quad \text{and} \quad x_2 \in C_i = [b_j, a_{j+1}], \quad j > i$$

If $\bar{f}$ is the united extension of f, then

$$\bar{f}(X) = \bar{f}([x_1, b_i]) \cup \bar{f}(C_i) \cup \cdots \cup \bar{f}(B_j) \cup \bar{f}([b_j, x_2])$$

Thus, in any case, with the terms that occur depending upon the type of interval (a "B_i" or a "C_i") in which the endpoints x_1, x_2 of $x = [x_1, x_2]$ fall, each interval $X \subset A$ can be represented (even by the computer) as a finite union of intervals, $D_1 \cup D_2 \cup D_2 \cdots \cup D_K, K \leq N$, with each D_i either equal to or contained in one of the intervals $B_j, C_j, j = 1, 2, \ldots, N$. The sign of f' is constant in each C_i and can be determined by the computer, say $f'(x) = (-1)^{S_i}|f'(x)|$ in C_i; if $f'(x) > 0$ (x in C_i), then $S_i = 0$; if $f'(x) < 0$ (x in C_i), then $S_i = 1$.

We can now describe an interval-valued function F on intervals $X \subset A$ such that $F(X) \supset \bar{f}(X)$, using these decompositions of intervals X in A as follows:

(1) Determine a representation of X using (6-12) so that

$$X = D_1 \cup D_2 \cup \cdots \cup D_K, \quad K \leq N$$

The right endpoint of D_i coincides with the left endpoint of D_{i+1}, and each D_i is contained (not necessarily properly) in a B_j or in a C_j.

(2) If $D_i = [y_1, y_2] \subset C_j$, then put

$$F([y_1, y_2]) = \begin{cases} [f(y_1), f(y_2)] & \text{if } S_j = 0 \\ [f(y_2), f(y_1)] & \text{if } S_j = 1 \end{cases} \tag{6-13}$$

If $D_i = [y_1, y_2] \subset B_j$, then evaluate in interval arithmetic one of the interval forms $F(X')$ of $f(x)$, say the centered form or the mean-value form with $X' = [y_1, y_2]$.

(3) Compute the union

$$F(X) = F(D_1) \cup F(D_2) \cup \cdots \cup F(D_K) \tag{6-14}$$

from left to right. Since $D_1 \cap D_2$ is nonempty, so is $F(D_1) \cap F(D_2)$, and so on.

PROBLEM 6.2 Apply the techniques of this section to the derivation of an expression $F(X)$ containing $\bar{f}(X)$, for $f(x) = x(1 - x)$, and all $X \subset [0, 1]$.

There is one application of the method just discussed which is especially important. That is the evaluation of the range of values of *integer powers of real numbers* lying in an interval. If $f(x) = x^n$ for a positive integer $n > 1$, then straightforward interval arithmetic does not give the exact range of values. For example,

$$[-1, 1] \cdot [-1, 1] = [-1, 1] \quad \text{whereas} \quad \{x^2 | x \in [-1, 1]\} = [0, 1]$$

By applying the notions of extreme values and using (6-14) we can define (and program for the computer) the computation of $\bar{f}(X)$, for $f(x) = x^n$, according to the following: if n is a positive integer, and $X = [x_1, x_2]$, then we define X^n by

$$X^n \equiv \begin{cases} [x_1^n, x_2^n] & \text{if } x_1 > 0 \\ \begin{cases} [0, \max(x_1^n, x_2^n)] & \text{if } 0 \in [x_1, x_2] \\ & \text{and } n \text{ is even} \\ [x_1^n, x_2^n] & \text{if } 0 \in [x_1, x_2] \\ & \text{and } n \text{ is odd} \end{cases} \\ \begin{cases} [x_2^n, x_1^n] & \text{if } x_2 < 0 \\ & \text{and } n \text{ is even} \\ [x_1^n, x_2^n] & \text{if } x_2 < 0 \\ & \text{and } n \text{ is odd} \end{cases} \end{cases}$$

and we have $X^n = \{x^n | x \in X\}$.

While we seem to be back to unions again in this section, there is an enormous difference between the practicality of results here and those obtained in Chapter 4 using unions. The distance $d(F(X), \bar{f}(X))$ using (6-14) can be made arbitrarily small by getting narrow enough intervals $B_1, B_2, \ldots, B_N$ containing the roots of f', so that for convergence we need not take more terms in the union (6-14) but, essentially, only need to improve the accuracy of the determination of the roots of f'. Of course, in (6–13) the indicated evaluations of f, namely $f(y_1), f(y_2)$, should, in practice, be carried out by the computer in rounded-interval arithmetic and the appropriate endpoint chosen; for example, to get $[f(y_1), f(y_2)]$ on the machine we compute $f(y_1)$ and $f(y_2)$ for rational f in rounded-interval arithmetic and take the resulting left endpoint of $f(y_1)$ and the right endpoint of $f(y_2)$ as the rounded-interval arithmetic version of $[f(y_1), f(y_2)]$. The same remarks apply to the definition of X^n. To make $d(F(X), \bar{f}(X))$ arbitrarily small we would have to use high enough precision in the rounded-interval arithmetic evaluations of $f(y_1), f(y_2)$.

For rational functions of several variables, the use of extreme values can again be made to derive an expression suitable for the machine computation of upper and lower bounds to the range of values over n-dimensional rectangles, i.e., over interval vectors.

Suppose $f(x_1, x_2, \ldots, x_n)$ is real-valued and rational in each real variable $x_1, \ldots, x_n$ and has no singularities in an n-dimensional rectangle $A = A_1 \otimes A_2 \otimes \cdots \otimes A_n, A_i \in \mathcal{I}$.

If f has an extreme value, in particular a local maximum or a local minimum at a point $p = (p_1, p_2, \ldots, p_n)$ in A, then

$$\frac{\partial f}{\partial x_i}(p_1, p_2, \ldots, p_n) = 0, \qquad i = 1, 2, \ldots, n \tag{6–15}$$

It is possible for the system of equations (6–15) to have whole continuums of solutions in the interior of A. For example, if $A_1 = A_2 = [-2, 2]$ and $f(x_1, x_2) = (x_1^2 + x_2^2 - 1)(x_1^2 + x_2^2 - 2)$, then (6–15) leads to

$$\frac{\partial f}{\partial x_1} = 2x_1(2(x_1^2 + x_2^2) - 3)$$

$$\frac{\partial f}{\partial x_2} = 2x_2(2(x_1^2 + x_2^2) - 3)$$

so that

$$\frac{\partial f_1}{\partial x_1}(p_1, p_2) = \frac{\partial f_2}{\partial x_2}(p_1, p_2) = 0$$

for the isolated point $(p_1, p_2) = (0, 0)$ and also for the whole circle of points $\{(p_1, p_2) | p_1^2 + p_2^2 = \frac{3}{2}\}$ lying in the interior of $A = A_1 \otimes A_2$.

On the other hand, the value of f must be constant on such a continuum (curve or surface for a rational f) of solutions of (6–15). To see this, parametrize some curve $(x_1(s), x_2(s), \ldots, x_n(s))$ lying in such a continuum S and consider $f(x_1(s), x_2(s), \ldots, x_n(s))$ as a function of s. We have

$$\frac{df}{ds} = \frac{\partial f}{\partial x_1}\frac{dx_1}{ds} + \cdots + \frac{\partial f}{\partial x_n}\frac{dx_n}{ds} = 0$$

from (6–15), and therefore f is constant along the chosen curve. If S is connected, then there is such a curve connecting any two points in S. Therefore f is constant in S.

As a consequence we need only find a point (or a small n-dimensional rectangle containing a point) on each of the separate finite number of connected components of the totality of solutions of (6–15) in order to be able to bound the locally extreme values of f in the interior of A.

On the boundary of A we must solve a similar problem for each of the $(n - 1)$-dimensional faces of A. There are $2n$ such faces.

After isolating locally extreme values in each of their interiors we have left the same problem for the faces of the faces, and so on, until we arrive in $n - 1$ steps to 1-dimensional faces, or edges, where we know what to do from (6–14).

There are altogether

$$2n + 2n \left(\frac{2(n - 1)}{2} \right) + 2n \left(\frac{2(n - 1)}{2} \right) \left(\frac{2(n - 2)}{3} \right)$$
$$+ \cdots 2n(2^{n-2}) = 3^n - 2^n - 1$$

such faces of various dimensions from $n - 1$ to 1 and, in particular, $n2^{n-1}$ edges involved.

On the other hand, it may not be necessary to carry out the complete reduction through faces of all dimensions from n to 1.

It can happen on each of the set of faces of a given dimension or even on A itself that one of the functions $(\partial f/\partial x_i)(x_1, x_2, \ldots, x_n)$ is of constant sign, say positive, and this information can be used to eliminate much of the boundary of A from further consideration.

Also, independent of the behavior of $\partial f/\partial x_i$ on the boundary of A, we can always decide arbitrarily to stop the process at faces of a given dimension (even $n - 1$, of which there are only $2n$), and bound the function f over these remaining parts of A by using interval arithmetic directly.

We will illustrate some of these remarks by reconsidering an example taken from Chapter 4 above, namely, the determination of the range of values of

$$f(x_1, x_2, x_3, x_4) = \frac{x_1}{x_1 x_2 - x_3 x_4} \tag{6–16}$$

for

$$x_1 \in A_1 = [.999, 1.01], \qquad x_2 \in A_2 = [.999, 1.01]$$
$$x_3 \in A_3 = [-10^{-3}, 10^{-3}], \qquad x_4 \in A_4 = [-10^{-3}, 10^{-3}]$$

See (4–4) and (4–10), (4–11).

In this example, we have the four-dimensional rectangle $A = A_1 \otimes A_2 \otimes A_3 \otimes A_4$. From (6–16), we find that

$$\frac{\partial f}{\partial x_1} = \frac{-x_3 x_4}{(x_1 x_2 - x_3 x_4)^2}$$

$$\frac{\partial f}{\partial x_2} = \frac{-x_1^2}{(x_1 x_2 - x_3 x_4)^2}$$

$$\frac{\partial f}{\partial x_3} = \frac{x_1 x_4}{(x_1 x_2 - x_3 x_4)^2}$$ (6-17)

$$\frac{\partial f}{\partial x_4} = \frac{x_1 x_3}{(x_1 x_2 - x_3 x_4)^2}$$

From (6-17) we find, according to (6-15), that locally extreme values of f may only occur in the interior of A at points (p_1, p_2, p_3, p_4) in A where

$$p_3 p_4 = 0 \quad and \quad p_1^2 = 0 \quad and \quad p_1 p_4 = 0 \quad and \quad p_1 p_3 = 0$$

equivalently, where

$$p_1 = 0 \quad and \quad p_3 = 0 \qquad or \qquad p_1 = 0 \quad and \quad p_4 = 0$$

These are two continuums of points of the forms

$$(0, p_2, 0, p_4) \qquad and \qquad (0, p_2, p_3, 0)$$

for all $p_2 \in A_2, p_3 \in A_3, p_4 \in A_4$.

Each of these two-dimensional planes intersects the boundary of A, since any (p_1, p_2, p_3, p_4) with any component at an endpoint of its containing interval is on the boundary of A.

Therefore, the maximum and minimum values of f are assumed in the boundary of A, in this example.

There are eight three-dimensional faces of A determined by setting one of the coordinates x_1, x_2, x_3, x_4 equal to an endpoint of its containing interval. One of these faces, for example, is obtained by setting $x_1 = .999$, giving the set of points

$$S_1 = \{(.999, x_2, x_3, x_4) | x_2 \in A_2, x_3 \in A_3, x_4 \in A_4\}$$

On S_1, f has the restricted form

$$f|_{S_1}(x_2, x_3, x_4) = \frac{.999}{.999 x_2 - x_3 x_4}$$

Again we examine partial derivatives;

$$\frac{\partial f|_{S_1}}{\partial x_2} = \frac{-(.999)^2}{(.999 x_2 - x_3 x_4)^2}$$

$$\frac{\partial f|_{S_1}}{\partial x_3} = \frac{.999 x_4}{(.999 x_2 - x_3 x_4)^2}$$

$$\frac{\partial f|_{S_1}}{\partial x_4} = \frac{.999 x_3}{(.999 x_2 - x_3 x_4)^2}$$

From the fact that $\partial f|_{S_1}/\partial x_2 < 0$ on S_1, we conclude that there are no extreme points of f in the interior of S_1 but, in fact, that the minimum of f on S_1 occurs for $x_2 = 1.01$ and the maximum value of f on S_1 occurs for $x_2 = .999$. Thus the minimum of f on S_1 must occur on the two-dimensional face

$$S_{1,1} = \{(.999, 1.01, x_3, x_4)|x_3 \in A_3, x_4 \in A_4\}$$

On $S_{1,1}$ the function f has the further restricted form

$$f|_{S_{1,1}}(x_3, x_4) = \frac{.999}{(.999)(1.01) - x_3 x_4} \tag{6-18}$$

At this point we can choose to evaluate the straightforward interval version of (6–18), obtaining

$$f|_{S_{1,1}}(A_3, A_4) \subset \frac{.999}{(.999)(1.01) - [-10^{-3}, 10^{-3}][-10^{-3}, 10^{-3}]}$$

$$\subset [.990018, \text{_____}]$$

and therefore the value of f on S_1 cannot be less than .990018.

By continuing the examination of the other faces of A we could find, in a number of ways which could be programmed for the computer, upper and lower bounds to the range of values of f on A.

PROBLEM 6.3. Using interval arithmetic directly, evaluate f as given by (6–16) on each of the three-dimensional faces of A and deduce, from these intervals, upper and lower bounds to the range of values of f on A.

PROBLEM 6.4. What is the range of values of

$$f(x) = \frac{ax + bx^2}{a + cx^3}$$

when $x = 2, a \in [4.1, 4.2], b \in [-2, -1.9], c \in [1, 1.1]$?

*PROBLEM 6.5. Write a program for bounding the range of values of a rational function of a single variable based on the methods of this section and making use of the root-finding methods of the next chapter.

6.5 VALUES AND RANGES OF VALUES OF IRRATIONAL FUNCTIONS

A number of the most commonly used irrational real functions are monotonic: exponentials, roots, powers, logarithms, arctangent, and so on. Given a computer subroutine of *known* accuracy for such a function f, the machine value f^* resulting from the subroutine satisfies

$$|f^*(x) - f(x)| \le \epsilon(x) \qquad \text{with } \epsilon(x) \text{ known}$$

If $f(x)$ is a monotonic-increasing function, such as

$$f(x) = x^{1/2}, \qquad x \geq 0$$

then an interval extension of f can be defined for $x = [x_1, x_2]$ by

$$F(X) = [f^*(x_1), f^*(x_2)] + [-\epsilon(x), \epsilon(x)] \qquad (6\text{-}19)$$

For many other commonly used functions—sine, cosine, the Bessel functions "J_0," "J_1," and so on—there is a sequence of adjacent intervals in which the functions are alternately monotonic increasing and decreasing. These successive intervals are separated by points at which the functions have locally extreme values—maxima and minima, successively—and the locations of these points are *known*. They are known in the sense that π is known, that is, arbitrarily narrow intervals can be computed containing them.

Using a procedure similar to that described in Section 6.4 [in particular by (6-14)], together with (6-19) (and its complementary version for decreasing functions) in place of (6-13), computer programs can be (and, in fact, have been) written for interval versions of the "elementary" functions sine (and cosine) such that, if $f(x) = \sin x$, then $F(X)$ is programmed so that

$$F(X) \supset \{\sin x \mid x \in X\}$$

By using high enough precision arithmetic and making $\epsilon(x)$ small enough in (6-19), the distance between $F(X)$ and $\bar{f}(X)$ for these piecewise monotonic real elementary functions can be made arbitrarily small.

In the case of each of the elementary functions a large number of properties are known, some of which are useful in making an efficient program for an interval extension. For example, the properties $|\sin x| \leq 1, |\cos x| \leq 1$ may be used to insure that the corresponding interval versions do not produce numbers greater than one in absolute value; the periodicity of these functions can be used, $\sin (x + 2\pi) = \sin x$, to reduce interval arguments down to a specified range of length 2π, say $[-\pi, \pi]$; similarly, $\exp (x) = \{\exp (x/N)\}^N$ can be used to scale down interval arguments of large magnitude for the interval exponential routine, and so on.

7 INTERVAL CONTRACTIONS AND ROOT-FINDING

7.1 INTRODUCTION

In this chapter we consider methods by which the computer can obtain intervals containing real zeros of rational functions. For a direct approach to finding circles in the complex plane containing zeros see, e.g., Champagne [1].

We shall discuss two general approaches (which can also be combined). One of these involves *interval contractions*, by which we mean interval functions F with the property that

$$F(X) \subset X \qquad (7\text{-}1)$$

If we also have, in addition to (7-1), the existence of a positive real number $R < 1$ such that

$$w(F(X)) \leq Rw(X)$$

then we will call F a *strong interval contraction*.

The application of interval contractions to the root-finding problem arises from the fact that by iterating an interval contraction F, a nested sequence of intervals results which converges to an interval containing a fixed point of the real restriction of F. If F is a strong interval contraction, then the sequence converges to a real number which is a fixed point of the real restriction of F. In any case, the sequence defined by

$$X_{n+1} = F(X_n)$$

satisfies $X_0 \supset X_1 \supset X_2 \supset \cdots \supset X_n$, and if $F([x, x]) = f(x)$, then

$$f(x) = x, \qquad x \in X_0 \qquad (7\text{-}2)$$

implies $x \in X_n, n = 1, 2, \ldots$.

If f has the fixed point x satisfying (7–2), then $g(x) = f(x) - x$ has x as a root and conversely. Given a function g whose roots we wish to bound in intervals, it may be possible to find a function h different from zero at the roots of g and such that $f(x) = h(x)g(x) + x$, which then has fixed points at the roots of g, can be used to construct an interval contraction.

A second approach amounts to a sort of "process of elimination" of regions or subintervals which we can determine do *not* contain any zeros of a given function. If f is a real rational function and F is a rational interval extension of f, i.e., the real restriction of F satisfies $F([x, x]) = f(x)$; and if $F([a, b])$ is defined, then we can seek subintervals of $[a, b]$, say X_1, $X_2, \ldots$, such that $F(X_1), F(X_2), \ldots$ are intervals which do *not* contain zero. In this way, by removing from $[a, b]$ intervals on which F is positive or negative, we can, perhaps, be left with a few narrow subintervals of $[a, b]$ in which f *may* have zeros. Furthermore, if

$$F(X_1) < 0 \quad and \quad F(X_2) > 0 \qquad or \qquad F(X_1) > 0 \quad and \quad F(X_2) < 0$$

and $X_1 < X_2$ then f *must*, by continuity, have a zero between X_1 and X_2. Figure 7.1 illustrates this situation. The curve in the figure is supposed to be the graph of the real rational function f. An interval extension F is assumed to have the property $F(X) \supset \bar{f}(X)$.

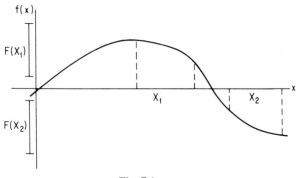

Fig. 7.1

7.2 INTERVAL CONTRACTIONS—FUNCTIONS OF A SINGLE VARIABLE

We will consider first real rational functions of a single real variable. Then we will take up methods for vector functions, i.e., the location of simultaneous zeros of systems of functions of several variables.

Suppose $f(x)$ is rational in the real variable x and that $f(x)$ is bounded on $x \in [a, b]$. Then f has a continuous derivative f' on $[a, b]$ and for $x, y \in [a, b]$ we have, from the mean-value theorem,

$$f(x) = f(y) + f'(y + \theta(x - y))(x - y) \tag{7-3}$$

for some $\theta \in [0, 1]$. If x is a zero of f, *and* if f' has a constant sign on $[a, b]$ (i.e., no zeros), then

$$x = y + \left(\frac{1}{-f'(y + \theta(x - y))} \right) f(y) \tag{7-4}$$

Thus y is a fixed point of the function on the right-hand side of (7-4) if and only if it is a zero of f.

Suppose that F' is a rational interval extension of f': $\bar{f}'(X) \subset F'(X)$ and $f'(x) = F'([x, x])$.

For $X \subset [a, b]$, and $m(X) =$ the midpoint of X, we define the interval function N (for "Newton") by

$$N(X) = m(X) + \left(\frac{1}{-F'(X)} \right) f(m(X)) \tag{7-5}$$

Approximating θ by 0 in (7-4) gives rise to Newton's method for approximating roots by iteration of the function on the right-hand side of (7-4). The equation (7-5) can be used in a similar fashion to provide an "interval version" of Newton's method, namely by choosing X_0 and defining the sequence of intervals $X_1, X_2, \ldots$ with

$$X_{n+1} = N(X_n) \cap X_n \tag{7-6}$$

As an illustration, we apply (7-5), (7-6) to the function $f(x) = x^2 - 2$, with $X_0 = [1, 2]$. We obtain, using $F'(X) = 2X$,

$$N(X) = m(X) - \frac{(m(X))^2 - 2}{2X}$$

Therefore, from (7-6), we obtain

$$X_1 = \frac{3}{2} - \frac{\frac{9}{4} - \frac{8}{4}}{[2, 4]} = \left[\frac{22}{16}, \frac{23}{16} \right]$$

We observe that $X_1 \subset X_0$.

Continuing, we compute [from (7-6)]

$$X_2 = \frac{45}{32} + \frac{1}{128} + \left[0, \frac{1}{2816} \right]$$

$$= [1.41406\ldots, 1.41441\ldots]$$

$$X_3 = [1.414213559\ldots, 1.414213566\ldots]$$

$$\vdots$$

For this example, the interval version of Newton's method (7-5), (7-6) gives a very rapidly contracting sequence of intervals containing $\sqrt{2}$.

In case we wish to find intervals containing the roots of a rational function f which has coefficients known only to lie in certain intervals, we can take an interval extension F which evaluates the range of values of f over the intervals of coefficients and use in place of (7–5) the more general form

$$N(X) = m(X) - \frac{F(m(X))}{F'(X)} \qquad (7\text{--}7)$$

For example, if we wish to find the roots of $f(x) = x^2 - c$ which are in the interval $[1, 2]$, for all $c \in [2, 3]$, we can put

$$F(X) = X^2 - [2, 3]$$
$$F'(X) = 2X$$
$$X_0 = [1, 2]$$

and, using (7–7), we find $N(X_0) \subset [1.39, 1.76]$. After one application of (7–6), we thus have

$$\{x | x^2 - c = 0, c \in [2, 3]\} \cap [1, 2] = [\sqrt{2}, \sqrt{3}] \subset [1.39, 1.76]$$

We investigate now some general properties of the interval mappings (7–5) and (7–7).

First of all, it is clear that if f' has a zero in $X = [x_1, x_2]$ then $F'(X) \supset \bar{f}'(x)$ is an interval containing zero so that $N(X)$ is not defined. As a consequence, if f has two *distinct* zeros in X, then f' must have a zero in between and $N(X)$ is not defined. Furthermore, $f'(x) = 0$ at a multiple root of f. As a result, we have the following:

LEMMA 7.1. A necessary condition for $N(X)$ to be defined by (7–5) is that X contain at most one zero of f and that such a zero be a simple root, i.e., not simultaneously a zero of f and f'.

For both (7–5) and (7–7) a sufficient condition that $N(X)$ be defined is, of course, that $F'(X)$ not contain zero and that $F(m(X))$ be defined.

Next, we have the following:

LEMMA 7.2. If $N(X)$ is defined by (7–5) for an interval X which contains a simple root of f, say $f(x) = 0, x \in X$, then $x \in N(X)$.

Proof. If $m(X) = x$, then (7–5) gives $N(X) = x$. Otherwise, suppose $m(X) > x$ and consider the interval $[x, m(X)]$. Because f' is continuous in $[x, m(X)]$ it follows from the mean-value theorem that for some y in the interval $[x, m(X)] \subset X$ the equation $f(m(X)) = f'(y)(m(X) - x)$ holds. Therefore

$$x = m(X) - \frac{f(m(X))}{f'(y)} \qquad \text{for some } y \in X$$

and, since $f'(y) \in F'(X)$, we conclude from (7–5) that $x \in N(X)$. The case left to be considered, when $m(X) < x$, can be treated the same way as the case $x < m(X)$ and the *lemma* is proved.

As a consequence of Lemma 7.2, we know that if X contains a zero of f, so does $N(X)$ whenever $N(X)$ is defined. Therefore, when $N(X)$ is defined we have one of the two following situations:

LEMMA 7.3. Either $N(X) \cap X$ is empty, in which case X does not contain a zero of f, or else $N(X) \cap X$ is an interval which *contains a zero of f if X does*.

We can use Lemma 7.3 to compute intervals of nonzeros of f [i.e., x is a "nonzero" of f if $f(x) \neq 0$] as well as to narrow down intervals which *may* contain a zero of f.

Given a real rational function f of a single real variable x with f bounded on an interval $[a, b]$, suppose we wish to find a set of "adjacent" intervals

$$[a, a_1], [a_1, a_2], \ldots, [a_{n-1}, a_n], [a_n, b]$$

with $a < a_1 < a_2 < \cdots < a_n < b$ which alternately *may* contain and *do not* contain a zero of f.

There are undoubtedly a great many schemes which could be programmed for the computer to do this. We will outline a procedure based on the previous discussion of this chapter.

Suppose we have an interval extension of f, say F, such that $F(X) \supset \bar{f}(X)$ for $X \subset [a, b]$, and an interval extension F' such that $F'(X) \supset \bar{f}'(X)$ for $X \subset [a, b]$. A procedure for decomposing the interval $[a, b]$ as described above can be programmed with the following steps:

(1) Evaluate $F([a, b])$ and $F'([a, b])$.

If $F([a, b])$ does not contain zero, then the process is complete for $[a, b]$. Otherwise, $F([a, b])$ contains zero and *may* contain a zero of f.

If $0 \in F([a, b])$, then $F'([a, b])$ may contain 0. If it does, perform step (2).

(2) Put $[a, b] = [a, (a + b)/2] \cup [(a + b)/2, b]$ and begin the whole process again at step (1) with each of the two subintervals.

If $F'([a, b])$ does not contain zero,

(3) Evaluate $N([a, b])$ from (7-7).

From Lemma 7.3, either $N([a, b]) \cap [a, b]$ is empty and $[a, b]$ does not contain a zero of f and the process is complete for $[a, b]$, or else $N(X) \cap X$ is an interval which may contain a zero of f for $X = [a, b]$.

In case $N([a, b]) \cap [a, b]$ from step (3) is an interval then

(4) Put $[a, b] = X_1 \cup X_2$, where $X_1 = N([a, b]) \cap [a, b]$.

The interval X_2 does not contain a zero of f and so the process is complete for X_2 (which we add to the collection of subintervals into which we are decomposing the original interval, $[a, b]$).

For the interval X_1 from step (4) we repeat the whole process beginning with step (1).

(5) Whenever an interval Y is found which does not contain a zero of f but which intersects with another such interval X already found, the two are "coalesced" into the single interval $X \cup Y$.

The process is carried on until, *for the precision used in the rounded-interval arithmetic*, no further improvement is made in expanding intervals of nonzeros or until some other appropriate criterion for stopping is met.

We now give an example of the application of the process just described. Consider the polynomial f given by

$$f(x) = x^3 - 5x^2 + 8x - 4$$

We have

$$f'(x) = 3x^2 - 10x + 8$$

Suppose we wish to use the above process to find the zeros of f which are in the interval $[0, 3]$.

We will use the nested forms of interval extensions,

$$F(X) = -4 + X(8 + X(X - 5))$$

$$F'(X) = 8 + X(3X - 10)$$

Applying step (1), we obtain $F([0, 3]) = [-25, 20]$ and $F'([0, 3]) = [-22, 8]$. Since F and F' contain zero, we apply step (2) and obtain

$$[0, 3] = [0, \tfrac{3}{2}] \cup [\tfrac{3}{2}, 3]$$

and find again that F and F' both contain zero on each of these sub-intervals. Repeating step (2) for each, we obtain

$$[0, 3] = [0, \tfrac{3}{4}] \cup [\tfrac{3}{4}, \tfrac{3}{2}] \cup [\tfrac{3}{2}, \tfrac{9}{4}] \cup [\tfrac{9}{4}, 3]$$

For the subinterval $[0, \tfrac{3}{4}]$ we find that F contains zero but $F'([0, \tfrac{3}{4}]) = [\tfrac{1}{2}, 8]$. Computing $N([0, \tfrac{3}{4}]) = [.581, 3.686]$ and applying step (4), we find that the interval $[0, .581]$ does not contain a zero of f.

*PROBLEM 7.1. By hand or using the computer, further refine the interval $[0, 3]$ into subintervals not containing zeros of f and a set of complementary subintervals which may contain zeros for the illustration begun above using the procedure given in this section.

It is of interest to know whether in the case of a simple root x such that $f(x) = 0$, $f'(x) \neq 0$ the interval version of Newton's method given by (7-5) and (7-6) will converge rapidly at least for an interval $[x_1, x_2]$, containing x, of sufficiently narrow width. This is, indeed, the case for evaluation of

(7–5) in exact-interval arithmetic. Using rounded-interval arithmetic, the "convergence" may still be rapid but the interval widths will not usually converge to zero. Instead, an integer n will be reached such that $N(X_n) \cap X_n = X_n$.

For rational functions f with interval coefficients, using (7–7) we can still get $N(X_n) \cap X_n = X_n$, but the resulting interval, even for exact-interval arithmetic evaluation, will usually be wider than the interval of zeros of f corresponding to the intervals of values of coefficients.

The use of the centered form (Section 6.2) for F and F' can help narrow the resulting interval using (7–7) with (7–6) iteratively.

For exact-interval arithmetic evaluation of (7–5) we have the following:

LEMMA 7.4. Given a real rational function f of a single real variable x with rational interval extensions F, F' of f, f' respectively such that f has a simple zero y in an interval $[x_1, x_2]$ for which $F([x_1, x_2])$ is defined and $F'([x_1, x_2])$ is defined and does not contain zero, then (7–5), (7–6) give an interval version of Newton's method which is "asymptotically error-squaring," that is to say there is an interval $X_0 \subset [x_1, x_2]$ containing y and a positive real number K such that

$$w(X_{n+1}) \leq K(w(X_n))^2$$

Proof. For all real numbers $x \in [x_1, x_2]$ we have $f(x) = F(x), f'(x) = F'(x)$ and for all intervals $X \subset [x_1, x_2]$ we have $\bar{f}(X) \subset F(X)$, $\bar{f}'(X) \subset F'(X)$. Furthermore, $F(y) = 0$, $F'(y) \neq 0$ at the zero y of f in $[x_1, x_2]$.

We can write (7–5), in this case, as

$$N(X) = m(X) - \frac{F(m(x))}{F'(X)} \tag{7–5}$$

since we have $F(m(X)) = f(m(X))$. For convenience, we repeat (7–6):

$$X_{n+1} = N(X_n) \cap X_n \tag{7–6}$$

Without loss of generality we can assume that $F'(X) > 0$ for all $X \subset [x_1, x_2]$, since if $F'([x_1, x_2]) < 0$ we can multiply f by -1; then f' is also multiplied by -1 and (7–5) is unchanged and $-f$ has the same zero as f.

From Corollary 1 to Theorem 4.4 we know there is a positive real number K_1 such that for $y_1 \leq y \leq y_2$ we have

$$F'([y_1, y_2]) = F'(y) + K_1[-(y_2 - y_1), (y_2 - y_1)] \tag{7–8}$$

For any $[y_1, y_2]$ containing y, the zero of f, and such that $[y_1, y_2] \subset [x_1, x_2]$, we have [from (7–5), (7–8), and inclusion monotonicity of interval arithmetic]:

$$N([y_1, y_2]) \subset \frac{y_1 + y_2}{2} - \frac{F((y_1 + y_2)/2)}{F'(y) + K_1[-(y_2 - y_1), (y_2 - y_1)]} \tag{7–9}$$

For small enough $y_2 - y_1$, $F'(y) - K_1(y_2 - y_1)$ is positive, since $F'(y)$ is supposed to be positive, and we have, from (7-9),

$$w(N([y_1, y_2])) \leq \frac{2K_1|F((y_1 + y_2)/2)|(y_2 - y_1)}{(F'(y))^2 - K_1^2(y_2 - y_1)^2} \tag{7-10}$$

Since $y \in [y_1, y_2]$ and $F(y) = 0$, we have

$$\left| F\left(\frac{y_1 + y_2}{2}\right) \right| \leq |F'([y_1, y_2])| \left(\frac{y_2 - y_1}{2}\right)$$

and from (7-8) we can write

$$\left| F\left(\frac{y_1 + y_2}{2}\right) \right| \leq (F'(y) + K_1(y_2 - y_1)) \left(\frac{y_2 - y_1}{2}\right)$$

Substituting this bound in (7-10) we get

$$w(N([y_1, y_2])) \leq \left\{ \frac{K_1(F'(y) + K_1(y_2 - y_1))}{(F'(y))^2 - K_1^2(y_2 - y_1)^2} \right\}(y_2 - y_1)^2$$

For small enough $y_2 - y_1$ this can be written

$$w(N([y_1, y_2])) \leq \left(\frac{K_1}{F'(y)} + 1\right)(y_2 - y_1)^2$$

Therefore there is a positive real number $K \geq (K_1/F'(y)) + 1$ such that for small enough $y_2 - y_1$ we have

$$w(N([y_1, y_2])) \leq K(w([y_1, y_2]))^2 \tag{7-11}$$

Now, for any two intervals I, J with nonempty intersection, we have

$$w(I \cap J) \leq \min(w(I), w(J))$$

Therefore, choosing $X_0 = [y_1, y_2]$ to satisfy (7-11), it follows that

$$w(N(X_0) \cap X_0) \leq K(w(X_0))^2 \tag{7-12}$$

and, defining a sequence of intervals by (7-6), it also follows that

$$X_{n+1} \subset X_n \quad \text{and} \quad w(X_{n+1}) \leq w(N(X_n))$$

so from (7-11) we have, by induction,

$$w(X_{n+1}) \leq K(w(X_n))^2$$

and Lemma 7.4 is proved.

Using the notion illustrated by Fig. 7.1, we can modify the process for finding roots outlined above so that some of the subintervals found can be guaranteed to contain a zero. This amounts to testing the sign of f in two intervals of nonzeros separated by an interval possibly containing a zero. If the two bordering intervals produce *opposite* signs for f, then the one in between *does* contain a simple zero of f.

7.3 INTERVAL CONTRACTIONS—FUNCTIONS OF SEVERAL VARIABLES

In the example following equation (6–15) we have seen a pair of rational equations in two variables

$$2x_1(2(x_1^2 + x_2^2) - 3) = 0$$
$$2x_2(2(x_1^2 + x_2^2) - 3) = 0$$

possessing solutions consisting of an isolated point $(x_1, x_2) = (0, 0)$ and a whole circle of points

$$\{(x_1, x_2) | x_1^2 + x_2^2 = \tfrac{3}{2}\}$$

In general, for a function f mapping real n-vectors into real n-vectors, $f(x_1, x_2, \ldots, x_n) = (y_1, y_2, \ldots, y_n)$, say given by n real-valued functions of n variables,

$$y_i = f_i(x_1, x_2, \ldots, x_n), \qquad i = 1, 2, \ldots, n$$

the vector equation $f(x) = 0$, or correspondingly the system of equations

$$f_i(x_1, x_2, \ldots, x_n) = 0, \qquad i = 1, 2, \ldots, n \tag{7-13}$$

will have a (possibly empty) set of real n-vector solutions not necessarily consisting only of a finite number of isolated points even for polynomials $f_i(x_1, \ldots, x_n)$.

Actually, even in the case of *linear* functions

$$f_i(x_1, x_2, \ldots, x_n) = b_i + a_{i1}x_1 + \cdots + a_{in}x_n$$

as is well known, when the system (7–13) can be written in matrix form as

$$Ax + b = 0 \tag{7-14}$$

the totality of solutions may consist of:

(1) no solutions at all, if A is singular and b is not in the range of A regarded as a linear transformation of the vector space E^n;

(2) a single isolated point (vector), if A is nonsingular and b is any vector; or

(3) an entire r-dimensional hyperplane of points, if A is singular and b is in the range of A.

As we can conclude from our example above, the situation is even more complicated for the nonlinear rational functions $f_i(x_1, x_2, \ldots, x_n)$ in (7–13), since the set of all solutions may include various algebraic curves and surfaces and "hypersurfaces" of dimensions from 1 to $n - 1$ of more complicated nature than the hyperplanes of solutions of (7–14), in addition possibly to some isolated points.

If the rational functions f_i in (7–13) and their partial derivatives $\partial f_i/\partial x_i > i, j = 1, 2, \ldots, n$, are bounded (and hence continuous) on an n-

dimensional rectangle $A = A_1 \otimes A_2 \otimes \cdots \otimes A_{n'}$ then from the mean-value theorem (see Section 6.3) we have

$$f_i(y_1, y_2, \ldots, y_n) = f_i(x_1, x_2, \ldots, x_n) + \sum_{j=1}^{n} \frac{\partial f_i}{\partial x_j}\bigg|_{x + \theta_i(y-x)} (y_j - x_j) \quad (7\text{-}15)$$

with the partial derivatives evaluated at the point

$$(x_1 + \theta_i(y_1 - x_1), x_2 + \theta_i(y_2 - x_2), \ldots, x_n + \theta_i(y_n - x_n))$$

for some $\theta_i \in [0, 1]$.

If we use the vector notation $x = (x_1, x_2, \ldots, x_n)$, and so on, then we can write (7-15) as

$$f(y) = f(x) + J(x + \theta_i(y - x))(y - x) \quad (7\text{-}16)$$

where, by $J(x + \theta_i(y - x))$, we mean the matrix whose ith row consists of the elements $\partial f_i / \partial x_j$ evaluated at $x + \theta_i(y - x)$.

If y is a zero of f and J in (7-16) is a nonsingular matrix, then we have

$$y = x - (J(x + \theta_i(y - x)))^{-1} f(x) \quad (7\text{-}17)$$

Given rational interval extensions of f_i and $\partial f_i / \partial x_j$, $i, j = 1, 2, \ldots, n$, say F_i and $F_{i,j}$, we can define a rational interval extension of the elements of $J(x + \theta_i(y - x))$ by

$$\frac{\partial f_i}{\partial x_j}\bigg|_{x + \theta_i(y-x)} \subset F_{i,j}(X + [0, 1](Y - X))$$

for $x \in X$, $\theta_i \in [0, 1]$, $y \in Y$; where, by $x \in X$, for example, we mean

$$x_1 \in X_1, \quad x_2 \in X_2, \quad \ldots, \quad x_n \in X_n$$

and X is the interval vector $(X_1, X_2, \ldots, X_n)$.

We will denote by $J(X + [0, 1](Y - X))$ the interval matrix whose elements are $F_{i,j}(X + [0, 1](Y - X))$.

LEMMA 7-5. Suppose $x, y \in Y$ and y is a zero of f, and suppose for the interval vector Y we can find an interval matrix V which contains the inverses of all real matrices in $J(x + [0, 1](Y - x))$; then $y \in x - VF(x)$.

Lemma 7.5 follows easily from (7-17). As a result we can define an interval-vector version of Newton's method by putting $m(Y) = (m(Y_1), \ldots, m(Y_n))$ and defining a sequence of interval vectors $X_{(1)}, X_{(2)}, \ldots$ by

$$X_{(n+1)} = X_{(n)} \cap \{m(X_{(n)}) - V_n F(m(X_{(n)}))\} \quad (7\text{-}18)$$

where V_n is an interval matrix containing the inverses of real matrices in $J(X_{(n)})$. Since $Y \subset X$ implies $J(Y) \subset J(X)$, the matrices V_n for $n = 1, 2, \ldots$ are obtainable if V_0 is obtainable from $J(X_{(0)})$.

From Lemma 7.5, it follows that if y is a zero of f and $y \in X_{(0)}$, and (7-18) is computable for $n = 0$ and defines an interval matrix $X_{(1)}$, then

$$y \in X_{(n)} \quad \text{for} \quad n = 1, 2, \ldots \quad (7\text{-}19)$$

The requirement of nonsingularity of the matrices $J(x)$ for all $x \in X_0$ is a necessary condition for the obtainability of V_0. *A zero y of f satisfying (7–19) will be an isolated zero.*

The following example will serve to illustrate the application of (7–18):

Let f be the vector function on the (x_1, x_2)-plane given by $f = (f_1, f_2)$ with

$$f(x) \equiv \begin{cases} f_1(x_1, x_2) = x_1^2 + x_2^2 - 1 \\ f_2(x_1, x_2) = x_1 - x_2 \end{cases}$$

Put

$$F_1(X_1, X_2) = X_1^2 + X_2^2 - 1$$
$$F_2(X_1, X_2) = X_1 - X_2$$

as the interval extensions of f_1, f_2. Since

$$\frac{\partial f_1}{\partial x_1} = 2x_1, \quad \frac{\partial f_1}{\partial x_2} = 2x_2, \quad \frac{\partial f_2}{\partial x_1} = 1, \quad \frac{\partial f_2}{\partial x_2} = -1$$

put

$$F_{1,1}(X_1, X_2) = 2X_1, \qquad F_{1,2}(X_1, X_2) = 2X_2$$
$$F_{2,1}(X_1, X_2) = 1, \qquad F_{2,2}(X_1, X_2) = -1$$

Then $J(X)$ is the interval matrix

$$J(X) = \begin{pmatrix} 2X_1 & 2X_2 \\ 1 & -1 \end{pmatrix}$$

Real matrices in $J(X)$ are of the form

$$\begin{pmatrix} 2x_1 & 2x_2 \\ 1 & -1 \end{pmatrix}$$

and have the corresponding inverses

$$\begin{pmatrix} \dfrac{1}{2(x_1 + x_2)} & \dfrac{x_2}{(x_1 + x_2)} \\ \dfrac{1}{2(x_1 + x_2)} & \dfrac{-x_1}{x_1 + x_2} \end{pmatrix}$$

For this example, we will suppose that V is defined by

$$V(X) = \begin{pmatrix} \dfrac{1}{2(X_1 + X_2)} & \dfrac{X_2}{X_1 + X_2} \\ \dfrac{1}{2(X_1 + X_2)} & \dfrac{-X_1}{X_1 + X_2} \end{pmatrix} \tag{7-20}$$

Using $V(X_{(n)})$ given by (7–20) for V_n in (7–18), and starting with (in "column-vector" notation)

$$X_{(0)} = \begin{pmatrix} [\frac{1}{2}, 1] \\ [\frac{1}{2}, 1] \end{pmatrix}$$

we determine $X_{(1)}$ using (7–18) as follows:

$$m(X_{(0)}) = \begin{pmatrix} .75 \\ .75 \end{pmatrix}$$

$$F(m(X_{(0)})) = \begin{pmatrix} .125 \\ 0 \end{pmatrix}$$

$$V_0 = V(X_{(0)}) = \begin{pmatrix} [\tfrac{1}{4}, \tfrac{1}{2}] & [\tfrac{1}{4}, 1] \\ [\tfrac{1}{4}, \tfrac{1}{2}] & [-1, -\tfrac{1}{4}] \end{pmatrix}$$

$$V_0 F(m(X_{(0)})) = \begin{pmatrix} [.03125, .0625] \\ [.03125, .0625] \end{pmatrix}$$

$$X_{(1)} = X_{(0)} \cap \{m(X_{(0)}) - V_0 F(m(X_{(0)}))\} = \begin{pmatrix} [.6875, .71875] \\ [.6875, .71875] \end{pmatrix}$$

Continued iteration of (7–18) will produce a rapidly converging sequence of nested-interval vectors each containing the zero

$$\begin{pmatrix} 1/\sqrt{2} \\ 1/\sqrt{2} \end{pmatrix} = \begin{pmatrix} .7071 \ldots \\ .7071 \ldots \end{pmatrix}$$

At present we do not have a procedure for the systematic use of the algorithm defined by (7–18) and Lemma 7.5 to obtain rectangles of nonzeros and retangles possibly containing zeros of f in a given rectangle comparable to the procedure outlined in Section 7.3 for the determination of narrow intervals containing the possible zeros of f in a given interval.

We must leave this and the further study of properties of the algorithm (7–18) as an important and, perhaps, difficult objective of future research.

It is important because a good computer program for finding zeros and regions of nonzeros of a system of functions can be used, as we indicated in Section 6.4, for the machine determination of sharp bounds on the ranges of values of functions of several variables. This in turn can lead to good machine-computed bounds on the remainder terms in Taylor series expansions, for instance, as we will use them in a later chapter on machine solutions of differential equations.

REFERENCE

1. CHAMPAGNE, W.P., JR., "On finding roots of polynomials by hook or by crook," TTN–37, The University of Texas, Computation Center, 1964.

8 INTERVAL INTEGRALS

8.1 INTRODUCTION

In this chapter we consider integrals of real-valued functions and methods for the machine computation of intervals containing the values of definite integrals.

We begin with a general procedure applicable to any continuous function f for which an interval extension F can be computed.

Suppose that F is an interval-valued function defined for $X \subset A$ where A is some interval $A = [a, b]$ with $a < b$ and that the real restriction of F is a continuous real-valued function f on A; $F(x) = f(x)$ for $x \in A$, and $\bar{f}(X) \subset F(X)$ for $X \subset A$.

By the fundamental theorem of calculus, the function g defined by

$$g(x) = \int_a^x f(x')\, dx', \qquad x \in [a, b] \tag{8-1}$$

has a continuous derivative $g'(x) = f(x)$ and, applying the mean-value theorem, we obtain

$$g(x) = g(a) + f(a + \theta(x - a))(x - a) \tag{8-2}$$

for some $\theta \in [0, 1]$. Since $g(a) = 0$, we can write (8-2) in the form

$$g(x) = \int_a^x f(x')\, dx' = f(a + \theta(x - a))(x - a) \tag{8-3}$$

for some $\theta \in [0, 1]$.

Using the interval extension F, we can write

$$g(x) = \int_a^x f(x')\, dx' \in F(a + [0, 1](x - a))(x - a)$$

70

and, since $x \in [a, b]$, we have $x \geq a$, so

$$\int_a^x f(x')\, dx' \in F([a, x])\, (x - a) \qquad (8\text{-}4)$$

From (8-4), it is clear that for any $X = [x_1, x_2] \subset A$, if we denote

$$\int_{x_1}^{x_2} f(x')\, dx'$$

by

$$\int_{[x_1, x_2]} f(x')\, dx' \qquad \text{or} \qquad \int_X f(x')\, dx'$$

we have

$$\int_X f(x')\, dx' \in F(X)w(X) \qquad (8\text{-}5)$$

Furthermore, by the "additivity" of the integral, we have

$$\int_{[x_1, x_2]} f(x')\, dx' + \int_{[x_2, x_3]} f(x')\, dx' = \int_{[x_1, x_3]} f(x')\, dx' \qquad (8\text{-}6)$$

and so

$$\int_{[x_1, x_3]} f(x')\, dx' \in F([x_1, x_2])\, (x_2 - x_1) + F([x_2, x_3])\, (x_3 - x_2)$$

for $x_1 < x_2 < x_3$.

For the case of a *rational interval function F*, we have the following:

THEOREM 8.1. *If* F *is a rational interval function defined for* $X \subset A$ *with real-valued real restriction* f *on* A *and if*

$$X_i^{(n)} = \left[a + \frac{i-1}{n}(x - a),\, a + \frac{i}{n}(x - a) \right], \qquad i = 1, 2, \ldots, n$$

then there is a positive real number K *such that for every positive integer* n,

$$\int_{[a, x]} f(x')\, dx' \in \sum_{i=1}^n F(X_i^{(n)}) \left(\frac{x - a}{n} \right) \qquad (8\text{-}7)$$

and

$$w \left(\sum_{i=1}^n F(X_i^{(n)}) \left(\frac{x - a}{n} \right) \right) \leq \frac{K(x - a)^2}{n} \qquad (8\text{-}8)$$

Proof. The relation (8-7) follows immediately from (8-5) and (8-6).

From a corollary to Theorem 4.4, we know there is a positive K such that for all $X \subset A$, $w(F(X)) \leq Kw(X)$, therefore

$$w \left(\sum_{i=1}^n F(X_i^{(n)}) \left(\frac{x - a}{n} \right) \right) \leq \left(\frac{x - a}{n} \right) \sum_{i=1}^n Kw(X_i^{(n)})$$

and, since $w(X_i^{(n)}) = (x - a)/n$, we obtain (8-8), and Theorem 8.1 is proved.

More generally, it follows from the definition and properties of the Riemann integral that for a function $f\colon A(\subset E^n) \to E^n$ which is continuous and has a uniform Lipschitz constant over a region A in E^n(n-dimensional Euclidean space), where A has a definite volume V and can be represented by finite unions of interval vectors

$$X_{(i)} = (X_{(i),1}, X_{(i),2}, \ldots, X_{(i),n})$$

$$A = \bigcup_{i=1}^{m} X_{(i)}$$

and

$$\sum_{i=1}^{m} \left(\prod_{j=1}^{n} w(X_{(i),j}) \right) = V$$

that for an interval extension F defined for interval vectors $X \subset A$ we have

$$\int_{p \in A} f(p)\, dV \equiv \int_A f(x_1, x_2, \ldots, x_n)\, dx_1 dx_2 \cdots dx_n \in S$$

where

$$S = \sum_{i=1}^{m} \left(F(X_{(i)}) \prod_{j=1}^{n} w(X_{(i),j}) \right) \tag{8-9}$$

and, furthermore, there is a positive K such that

$$w(S) \leq KV \max_i w(X_{(i)}) \tag{8-10}$$

Formula (8–7), like the method of Chapter 4 involving unions, is a "first-order" method and is of little practical value for machine computations in comparison with higher-order methods such as we will describe in the next section.

On the other hand, formulas (8–5) and (8–9) provide a basis for the concept and definition of an *interval integral*, i.e., an interval-valued integral of interval-valued functions [2].

Suppose f is a continuous *interval-valued function* of a real variable—for example, a rational function of x—but with interval coefficients rather than real ones. If we have a continuous interval extension F of the function f, $F(x) = f(x)$, then we define the *integral* of f by

$$\int_{[a,x]} f(x')\, dx' = \bigcap_{n=1}^{\infty} \sum_{i=1}^{n} F(X_i^{(n)}) \left(\frac{x-a}{n} \right) \tag{8-11}$$

with $X_i^{(n)}$ defined as in Theorem 8.1.

For each set, c, of real coefficients from the given interval vector C of coefficients of a rational f, we obtain a continuous real-valued function f_c such that $f_c(x) \in f(x)$ and, from (8–7),

$$\int_{[a,x]} f_c(x')\, dx'$$

is contained in the right-hand side of (8–11); therefore

$$\int_{[a,x]} f(x')\, dx' = \left\{ \int f_c(x')\, dx' \middle| c \in C \right\}$$

Put, perhaps, more simply, if f is a continuous interval-valued function of a real variable x in $[a, b]$, then there is a pair of continuous real-valued functions f_1, f_2 such that $f(x) = [f_1(x), f_2(x)]$ and our definition of the integral of f is equivalent to

$$\int_{[a,x]} f(x')\, dx' = \left[\int_{[a,x]} f_1(x')\, dx', \int_{[a,x]} f_2(x')\, dx' \right] \tag{8–12}$$

An advantage of the representation (8–11) over (8–12) is that our interval extensions (of real functions) are usually obtained not by directly representing endpoints as real functions, but by extending more or less directly the real operations defining a function to corresponding interval operations. Thus, for example, (8–11) explicitly shows a convergent computational algorithm for rational f.

PROBLEM 8.1. Using (8–7), find an interval containing the natural logarithm of 1.1 of width less than .05. Notice that

$$\log_e x = \int_1^x \frac{dx'}{x'}$$

How large must n be according to (8–8) so that $\log_e 2$ can be found to ten decimal places using (8–7)?

Notice that (8–11) or a repeated application of (8–7) can be used as a basis for computing iterated integrals of rational functions—for example,

$$\int_1^y \log_e x\, dx = \int_1^y \int_1^x \left(\frac{dx'}{x'} \right) dx \tag{8–13}$$

We have

$$\int_1^y \log_e x\, dx \in \sum_{i=1}^n F(Y_i^{(n)}) \left(\frac{y-1}{n} \right)$$

where

$$Y_i^{(n)} = 1 + \left[\frac{i-1}{n}, \frac{i}{n} \right] (y - 1)$$

and

$$F(Y_i^{(n)}) = \sum_{j=1}^m \left(\frac{1}{X_j^{(m)}(Y_i^{(n)})} \right) w(X_j^{(m)}(Y_i^{(n)}))$$

and

$$X_j^{(m)}(Y_i^{(n)}) = 1 + \left[\frac{j-1}{m}, \frac{j}{m} \right] (Y_i^{(n)} - 1)$$

A useful lemma in connection with interval integrals is the following.

LEMMA 8.1. If f and g are continuous interval-valued functions of a real variable $x \in [a, b]$ and if $f(x) \subset g(x)$, then

$$\int_{[a,b]} f(x)\, dx \subset \int_{[a,b]} g(x)\, dx$$

Proof. From (8–12), if $f(x) = [f_1(x), f_2(x)]$ and $g(x) = [g_1(x), g_2(x)]$, then $f(x) \subset g(x)$ implies

$$\int_{[a,b]} g_1(x)\, dx \leq \int_{[a,b]} f_1(x)\, dx \leq \int_{[a,b]} f_2(x)\, dx \leq \int_{[a,b]} g_2(x)\, dx$$

and Lemma 8.1 is proved.

For rational integrands, an approach to the machine computation of intervals containing exact values of definite integrals *could* be based on a "partial-fraction decomposition" of the integrand as a sum of rational functions with linear or quadratic polynomial denominators. Formidable complications arise in attempting a *general* computational program along such lines, so we will not pursue that approach here.

8.2 Kth-ORDER INTERVAL METHODS FOR DEFINITE INTEGRALS

In this section we discuss a method for computing intervals containing the value of the definite integral

$$\int_{[a,b]} f(x)\, dx$$

based on subdividing the interval $[a, b]$ into n subintervals and expanding the integrand in each subinterval in a Taylor series with remainder. The remainders are evaluated by interval computations; and, for uniform subdivision of $[a, b]$ into subintervals of width $h = (b - a)/n$, the method can be made of arbitrarily high order in the sense that the width of the interval result using exact-interval arithmetic can be made of order $O(h^K)$ for arbitrarily large positive integers K. The method is applicable, in particular, to rational integrands.

The evaluation of the remainder terms will require interval extensions of high-order derivatives of the given integrand. Efficient machine programs for the derivation and evaluation *by the computer* of interval extensions of high-order derivatives of functions are now available and will be described in a later chapter.

Suppose f is rational in x with real coefficients and

$$I = \int_{[a,b]} f(x)\,dx \tag{8-14}$$

and suppose $f^{(r)}$, $r = 1, 2, \ldots, K$, are the derivatives of f of order $r = 1$, $2, \ldots, K$. We define the "zeroth" derivative: $f^{(0)} \equiv f$.

If $F^{(r)}$, $r = 0, 1, 2, \ldots, K$ are rational interval extensions of $f^{(r)}$, $r = 0$, $1, 2, \ldots, K$, respectively, and if each $F^{(r)}$ is defined for all $X \subset [a, b]$, then the following formula can be evaluated in interval arithmetic:

$$I_{n,K} = \sum_{i=1}^{n} \sum_{r=0}^{K-1} \frac{F^{(r)}(x_{i-1})}{(r+1)!} \{w(X_i)\}^{r+1} + \frac{1}{(K+1)!} \sum_{i=1}^{n} F^{(K)}(X_i)\{w(X_i)\}^{K+1}$$

$$\tag{8-15}$$

where the interval $[a, b]$ has been subdivided so that

$$[a, b] = \bigcup_{i=1}^{n} X_i \qquad \text{with } X_i = [x_{i-1}, x_i]$$

We suppose that $a = x_0 < x_1 < \cdots < x_n = b$.

THEOREM 8.2. If I and $I_{n,K}$ are defined by (8-14), (8-15), then for all $n, K \geq 1$,

$$I \in I_{n,K} \tag{8-16}$$

and there exists a positive number L_K for each $K \geq 1$ such that

$$w(I_{n,K}) \leq L_K \{ \max_{i=1,2,\ldots,n} w(X_i)\}^{K+1}$$

Proof. The hypothesis stated in the definition of (8-15) that $F^{(r)}$ is defined for $X \subset [a, b]$ implies in particular that $f^{(r)}$ is bounded and continuous on $[a, b]$. From the Taylor theorem we obtain for each $t \in [0, w(X_i)]$

$$f(x_{i-1} + t) = f^{(0)}(x_{i-1}) + f^{(1)}(x_{i-1})t + \cdots$$

$$+ \frac{f^{(K-1)}(x_{i-1})t^{K-1}}{(K-1)!} + R_{i-1}^{\{K\}}(t) \tag{8-17}$$

with

$$R_{i-1}^{\{K\}}(t) = \frac{1}{K!} f^{(K)}(x_{i-1} + \theta_i t)t^K$$

for some $\theta_i \in [0, 1]$. From Lemma 8.1, we have

$$\int_{[0, w(X_i)]} R_{i-1}^{\{K\}}(t)\,dt \in \frac{1}{K!} \int_{[0, w(X_i)]} F^{(K)}(X_i)t^K\,dt$$

since

$$R_{i-1}^{\{K\}}(t) \in \frac{1}{K!} F^{(K)}(X_i)t^K \qquad \text{for } t \in [0, w(X_i)]$$

But we also have

$$\int_{[0,\,w(X_i)]} F^{(K)}(X_i)t^K\,dt = F^{(K)}(X_i)\int_{[0,\,w(X_i)]} t^K\,dt$$

so

$$\int_{[0,\,x(X_i)]} R^{\{K\}}_{i-1}(t)\,dt \in \frac{F^{(K)}(X_i)}{(K+1)!}\{w(X_i)\}^{K+1} \tag{8-18}$$

Integrating (8–17) term by term over $t \in [0, w(X_i)]$ and using (8–18), we obtain the result (8–15) by summing over $i = 1, 2, \ldots, n$.

Thus we have proved (8–16). For rational $F^{(K)}$ there is a positive number C_K independent of X such that $X \subset [a, b]$ implies

$$w(F^{(K)}(X)) \le C_K w(X) \tag{8-19}$$

For infinite-precision interval-arithmetic evaluation of (8–15) the only terms contributing to the *width* of $I_{n,K}$ are the $F^{(K)}(X_i)$. Using (8–19), we get

$$w(I_{n,K}) \le \frac{1}{(K+1)!} \sum_{i=1}^{n} C_K\{w(X_i)\}^{K+2}$$

Since, by definition, $X_i = [x_{i-1}, x_i]$ with $x_0 = a$, $x_n = b$, we have

$$\sum_{i=1}^{n} w(X_i) = b - a$$

and therefore

$$w(I_{n,K}) \le \frac{C_K(b-a)}{(K+1)!} \max_{i=1,2,\ldots,n}\{w(X_i)\}^{K+1} \tag{8-20}$$

This completes the proof of Theorem 8.2.

Notice that from (8–19) and (8–20) we may be able to get an explicit bound for L_K in Theorem 8.2 if we can find a C_K satisfying (8–19). For example, we can estimate C_K by

$$\frac{w(F^{(K)}([a, b]))}{w([a, b])}$$

in order to choose a pair of integers n, K which makes the bound on $w(I_{n,K})$ given by (8–20) small and then, by actual evaluation of (8–15) using *rounded*-interval arithmetic, we will obtain an interval $I_{n,K}$ which, at least, is guaranteed to contain the exact result (8–14) and whose width $w(I_{n,K})$ will be that of the machine-computed interval.

In a later chapter we will find that for rational functions f the number of arithmetic operations to get $F^{(r+1)}$ once the values of $F^{(0)}, F^{(1)}, \ldots, F^{(r)}$ have been computed increases at most linearly with r. Suppose we therefore estimate the "amount of computation time" required to get a value of $I_{n,K}$ using (8–15) by

$$T(I_{n,K}) = nK^2 T_0 \tag{8-21}$$

where T_0 is some positive constant. Furthermore, suppose we estimate the width of the interval $I_{n,K}$ which will result from evaluating (8–15) by

$$W(I_{n,K}) = \left(\frac{b-a}{n}\right)^{K+1} W_0 \qquad (8\text{--}22)$$

with $W_0 = w(F[a, b])$. If max $w(X_i)$ is nearly $(b-a)/n$, and if $w(F^{(K)}[a, b])$ $/(K+1)!$ does not vary too rapidly with K, say no more than θ^K for some θ near 1, then (8–22) will be a reasonably satisfactory estimate of $w(I_{n,K})$ for our purpose here.

What we wish to do now is use the a priori estimates of computation time (8–21) and accuracy (8–22) to obtain at least a rough idea of the "best" choice of n, K for (8–15) in the sense of minimizing $T(I_{n,K})$ among all choices of n, K for which $W(I_{n,K}) \leq \epsilon$, for a given $\epsilon > 0$. From (8–22), for a given $K \geq 1, b - a > 0, W_0 > 0$ we will have $W(I_{n,K}) \leq \epsilon$ for all $n \geq (b-a)(W_0/\epsilon)^{1/(K+1)}$. We define $N(K) = (b-a)(W_0/\epsilon)^{1/(K+1)}$ and substitute $N(K)$ into (8–21), treating K and $N(K)$, for the moment, as continuous variables. Then we obtain the expression $T(K) = N(K)K^2 T_0$ or

$$T(K) = (b-a) \left(\frac{W_0}{\epsilon}\right)^{1/(K+1)} K^2 T_0 \qquad (8\text{--}23)$$

and, differentiating (8–23) with respect to K, we get

$$T'(K) = (b-a)T_0 \left(\frac{W_0}{\epsilon}\right)^{1/(K+1)} \left\{2K - \left(\frac{K}{K+1}\right)^2 \log_e \left(\frac{W_0}{\epsilon}\right)\right\} \qquad (8\text{--}24)$$

We have the following cases:

(1) *For* $\epsilon \geq W_0$, we find from (8–24) that $T'(K) > 0$, so the choice of $n, K \geq 1$ which minimizes $T(K)$ is $K = 1$ with n chosen as the smallest integer satisfying

$$n \geq (b-a) \left(\frac{W_0}{\epsilon}\right)^{1/2} \qquad (8\text{--}25)$$

(2) *For* $\epsilon < W_0$, say $\log_e (W_0/\epsilon) = \alpha > 0$, $T'(K)$ has the same sign as the expression $2 - (K/(K+1)^2)\alpha$; in fact, for $\alpha > 0, T'(K)$ has the same sign as the expression

$$S(K) = \left(K + \frac{1}{K}\right) + \left(\frac{\alpha}{2} - 2\right) \qquad (8\text{--}26)$$

Since $K + 1/K \geq 2$, for $K \geq 1$, we conclude that $T'(K) > 0$ for $\alpha/2 - 2 < 2$, or $\alpha < 8$.

Thus we have the subcase

(2a) If $e^{-8}W_0 = (.000335...)W_0 < \epsilon < W_0$ (or $\alpha < 8$), then we again choose $K = 1$, and n as the smallest integer satisfying (8–25). The case $\alpha = 8$, or $\epsilon = e^{-8}W_0$, may be included in (2a) since the zero of $T'(K)$ for $\alpha = 8$ occurs at $K = 1$ and $T'(K) > 0$ for $K > 1$ when $\alpha = 8$.

Finally we have the subcase

(2b) For $8 < \alpha$ or $0 < \epsilon < e^{-8}W_0$, $S(K)$ given by (8–26) [and hence $T'(K)$], has two zeros one of which is greater than 1, namely

$$K = \frac{\alpha - 4}{4} + \frac{\sqrt{\alpha(\alpha - 8)}}{4} \tag{8-27}$$

For this case we choose the nearest integer to (8–27) and, for n, we take the smallest integer satisfying

$$n \geq (b - a)\left(\frac{W_0}{\epsilon}\right)^{1/(K+1)} \tag{8-28}$$

For very small ϵ, we would expect the last case, (2b), to occur.

In order to illustrate the result of using the procedure just described for choosing K and n to be used in (8–15), we consider the following example:

$$I = \int_{[0,t]} \frac{1}{1 + x^2}\, dx, \qquad t > 0$$

Thus in (8–14) we put $f(x) = 1/(1 + x^2)$ and $[a, b] = [0, t]$. For the derivatives of f, we find that

$$(1 + x^2)f(x) = 1$$

$$(1 + x^2)f^{(1)}(x) + (2x)f(x) = 0$$

$$\vdots \tag{8-29}$$

and for $r \geq 2$,

$$(1 + x^2)f^{(r)}(x) + r(2x)f^{(r-1)}(x) + \frac{r(r - 1)}{1.2}(2)f^{(r-2)}(x) = 0$$

From (8–29) we can recursively determine $f^{(r)}(x)$ for $r = 2, 3, \ldots$. For interval extensions $F^{(r)}$, we can put

$$F(X) = \frac{1}{1 + X^2}$$

$$F^{(1)}(X) = \frac{-2XF(X)}{1 + X^2}$$

and for $r \geq 2$ (from 8–29) we choose

$$F^{(r)}(X) = \left(\frac{-1}{1 + X^2}\right)\{2rXF^{(r-1)}(X) + r(r - 1)F^{(r-2)}(X)\} \tag{8-30}$$

We will, for simplicity, subdivide $[0, t]$ into subintervals X_i of equal width,

$$X_i = \left[\frac{(i - 1)t}{n}, \frac{it}{n}\right], \qquad i = 1, 2, \ldots, n$$

By properly arranging the sums in (8–15) we can use a nested evaluation of each of n polynomials in $w(X_i)$. Such a rearrangement is again an interval extension $I_{n,K}$ satisfying Theorem 8.2 and requires nK interval multiplications and additions besides those needed to obtain the coefficients. From the expressions above for $F^{(r)}$, in particular (8–30), we see that the number of operations to get $F^{(r)}$ from $F^{(r-1)}, F^{(r-2)}, \ldots$ goes up linearly with r for $r = 0, 1, 2$ and then remains constant.

Thus a more accurate estimate than (8–21) for this problem of the computation time would be

$$T(I_{n,K}) = \begin{cases} nK^2 T_0, & K \leq 2 \\ nT_0(4 + 4(K - 2)), & K > 2 \end{cases} \tag{8-31}$$

By modifying our procedure to use (8–31) in place of (8–21) in the derivation of a choice for n, K given ϵ, we would find (n_1, K_1) from (8–31) and (n_0, K_0) from (8–21) and we would have $K_1 > K_0$ when ϵ is very small. On the other hand, the machine evaluation of $I_{n,K}$ in finite-precision rounded-interval arithmetic will experience a "point of diminishing return" in $w(I_{n,K})$ for increasing K because of the build-up of *excess* width in the machine-computed intervals for the coefficients in (8–15) over the width of the corresponding exact-interval arithmetic result. This has the effect of guiding our choice of K back down from K_1 toward K_0.

In any case we will look at some choices for n, K made by the procedure we derived from (8–21) for the present example.

First of all, we have for $t > 0$

$$W_0 = w \left(\frac{1}{1 + [0, t]^2} \right) = 1 - \frac{1}{1 + t^2}$$

For our illustration we put $\epsilon = 10^{-6}$ and consider various values of t. We have

$$\alpha = \log_e \left(1 - \frac{1}{1 + t^2} \right) + 6 \log_e 10$$

or

$$\alpha = (13.81 \ldots) - \log_e \left(1 + \frac{1}{t^2} \right) \tag{8-32}$$

(1) *For very large t*, (8–32) gives $\alpha = 13.81 \ldots > 8$ and case (2b) using (8–27) and (8–28) gives $K = 5$ and $n \geq 10t$. Thus *for large t*, our procedure for choosing K, n says to use $K = 5$ in (8–15) with subintervals X_i of width about .1 in order to obtain, in something like the least computing time, an interval $I_{n,K}$ which will have a width about 10^{-6}.

(2) *For $t = 2$*, we find $\alpha = 13.6$ (approximately), and we would again choose $K = 5, n = 20$ by evaluating (8–27) and (8–28).

(3) Finally, *for very small t*, we have $W_0 = t^2$ (approximately); e.g., for $0 < t < .01$, say, we have $W_0 = (.9999 \ldots)t^2$ and $\alpha \leq 13.81 - \log_e 10^4 = 4.6 \ldots$. So from case (2a), with $\alpha < 8$, we choose $K = 1$ and n according to (8–25), which becomes

$$n \geq t \left(\frac{t^2}{10^{-6}}\right)^{1/2} = t^2 \cdot 10^3 \qquad (8\text{-}33)$$

and for $0 < t < .01$, the lower bound (8-33) on n is less than 1, therefore, for $t < .01$, the procedure chooses $n = K = 1$, as might be expected.

PROBLEM 8.2. Using $T(I_{n,K}) = nKT_0$ in place of (8-21), derive a procedure for choosing n, K to minimize $T(I_{n,K})$ subject to the constraint (8-28).

Many other quadrature formulas are available with a remainder term expressed in "mean-value form" such that by using interval extensions of the integrand and its derivatives through the order of the remainder term an interval version of the formula can be derived. Examples are the R-point Gaussian quadrature formulas, $R = 1, 2, \ldots$ (see [1]).

REFERENCES

1. MOORE, R. E., "The automatic analysis and control of error in digital computation based on the use of interval numbers," in L. B. Rall, ed., *Error in
   Digital Computation*, Vol. I, esp. pp. 76–88. New York: John Wiley & Sons,
   Inc., 1965.
2. MOORE, R. E., STROTHER, W., and YANG, C. T., "Interval integrals," LMSD-
   703073, Lockheed Missiles and Space Co., Palo Alto, California, 1960.

9 INTEGRAL EQUATIONS

9.1 INTRODUCTION

Consider an *integral equation* of the form

$$y(x) = h(x) + \int_{a(x)}^{b(x)} g(x, x', y(x')) \, dx' \tag{9-1}$$

for $a_0 \le a(x) < b(x) \le b_0$ with h, a, b defined for $x \in [a, b]$ and g defined for $x, x' \in [a_0, b_0]$ and $y \in [c, d]$. Suppose that the real valued functions a, b, h, g are all continuous and that g satisfies a Lipschitz condition in y, i.e., there is an $L > 0$ such that for all $x, x' \in [a_0, b_0]$; $y_1, y_2 \in [c, d]$ we have

$$|g(x, x', y_1) - g(x, x', y_2)| \le L|y_1 - y_2| \tag{9-2}$$

We can make the set of continuous real-valued functions on $[a_0, b_0]$ (usually denoted by $C[a_0, b_0]$) into a metric space with the distance function

$$d_M(f_1, f_2) = \max_{x \in [a, b]} |f_1(x) - f_2(x)| \tag{9-3}$$

We can regard the right-hand side of (9-1) as defining a mapping T which for each continuous function y on $[a_0, b_0]$ produces another such function $T(y)$. The integral equation (9-1) can be written in terms of the mapping T as

$$y = T(y) \tag{9-4}$$

Then a solution y of (9-1) is expressed as a "fixed point" of the mapping T. If T has the property that for the metric space M of all continuous functions on $[a, b]$ with values in $[c, d]$ we have $T(y) \in M$, and if there is an $L_1 < 1$ such that for all $y_1, y_2 \in M$,

$$d_M(T(y_1), T(y_2), < L_1 d_M(y_1, y_2) \tag{9-5}$$

81

then T is called a *strong-contraction* mapping on the metric space M (of continuous functions $y\colon [a_0, b_0] \to [c, d]$). Under these conditions, (9–5) implies the existence and uniqueness of a fixed point of T, i.e., a solution of (9–4). Furthermore, if $y_1 \in M$, then the sequence $y_{n+1} = T(y_n)$ of functions in M converges to the solution y of (9–4). This is usually proved as follows. From (9–5) we have

$$d_M(y_2, y_1) = d_M(T(y_1), y_1) \leq d - c$$

and for $n > 1$ we have

$$d_M(y_{n+1}, y_n) = d_M(T(y_n), T(y_{n-1})) \leq L_1 d_M(y_n, y_{n-1}) \tag{9–6}$$

therefore

$$d_M(y_{n+1}, y_n) \leq L_1^{n-1}(d - c)$$

Using the triangle inequality for the distance function d_M, we find that for $p \geq 1$

$$d_M(y_{n+p}, y_n) \leq L_1^{n-1}(1 + L_1 + L_1^2 + \cdots + L_1^p)(d - c)$$

thus for arbitrary $p \geq 1$ we have

$$d_M(y_{n+p}, y_n) \leq \frac{L_1^{n-1}}{1 - L_1}(d - c) \tag{9–7}$$

Since $L_1 < 1$, by hypothesis, the inequality (9–7) shows that $\{y_n\}$ is a Cauchy sequence in the *complete* metric space M and so a continuous function y exists in M to which the sequence $\{y_n\}$ converges uniformly. The uniqueness of y follows from (9–5) since $L_1 < 1$.

Interpreting these well-known results for (9–1), we find using (9–2), that for

$$T(y) = h(x) + \int_{a(x)}^{b(x)} g(x, x', y(x'))\, dx'$$

we will have $T(y) \in M$ if $y \in M$, and there will be an $L_1 < 1$ for which (9–5) is satisfied, provided $h(x)$ is interior to $[c, d]$, $c < h(x) < d$, for all $x \in [a_0, b_0]$, say $\bar{h}([a, b]) = [c_1, d_1]$ with $c < c_1 \leq d_1 < d$, and provided $b_0 - a_0$ is small enough. In fact, we can put $L_1 = (b_0 - a_0)L$, where L satisfies (9–2), and if $b_0 - a_0$ is small enough to make this $L_1 < 1$ and also small enough to make

$$[c_1, d_1] + (b_0 - a_0)\, \bar{g}([a_0, b_0], [a_0, b_0], [c, d]) \subset [c, d]$$

then (9–1) will have a unique solution which is the limit of the sequence of functions defined by

$$y_0(x) = \frac{c + d}{2}$$

and, for $n = 0, 1, 2, \ldots,$

$$y_{n+1}(x) = h(x) + \int_{a(x)}^{b(x)} g(x, x', y_n(x')) \, dx' \tag{9-8}$$

In the next section we will develop an interval version of these results.

The form of the integral equation (9-1) is general enough to include, for example, the initial-value problem

$$\frac{dy}{dx} = f(x, y), \qquad y(x_0) = y_0 \tag{9-9}$$

which can be written as the integral equation

$$y(x) = y_0 + \int_{x_0}^{x} f(x', y(x')) \, dx' \tag{9-10}$$

and also the two-point boundary problem, for $x_1 > x_0$,

$$\frac{d^2 y}{dx^2} = f(x, y), \qquad y(x_0) = y_0, \quad y(x_1) = y_1 \tag{9-11}$$

which can be written as the integral equation

$$y(x) = y_0 + \left(\frac{y_1 - y_0}{x_1 - x_0}\right)(x - x_0) + \int_{x_0}^{x_1} K(x, x')(x_1 - x_0) f(x', y(x')) \, dx' \tag{9-12}$$

where

$$K(x, x') = \begin{cases} \left(\dfrac{x - x_0}{x_1 - x_0} - 1\right)\left(\dfrac{x' - x_0}{x_1 - x_0}\right) & \text{for } x' \le x \\[3mm] \left(\dfrac{x' - x_0}{x_1 - x_0} - 1\right)\left(\dfrac{x - x_0}{x_1 - x_0}\right) & \text{for } x' > x \end{cases}$$

Analogous results are available for vector functions y, h, g in (9-1).

The form of (9-1) is certainly not the most general integral equation for which the iteration procedure converges based on the strong-contraction property (9-5). The reader is referred to works on integral equations and functional analysis for further discussion of such questions as well as for other methods of solving integral equations. It has been our purpose in this section to motivate the interval methods to be considered next.

9.2 AN INTERVAL METHOD FOR INTEGRAL EQUATIONS

Given an integral equation of the form (9-1), suppose we can find an interval extension G such that

$$G(x, x', y(x')) = g(x, x', y(x'))$$

and

$$G(x, x', y(x')) \supset \bar{g}(x, x', y(x'))$$

where $\bar{g}$ is the united extension of g (see Chapter 4) and $Y(x')$ is an interval-valued function with $Y(x') \subset [c, d]$. With the concept of an interval integral (Chapter 8) we can define a sequence of interval-valued functions of the real variable $x \in [a_0, b_0]$ by

$$Y_0(x) = [c, d]$$

and, for $n = 0, 1, 2, \ldots$,

$$Y_{n+1}(x) = h(x) + \int_{[a(x), b(x)]} G(x, x', Y_n(x')) \, dx' \qquad (9\text{-}13)$$

If G has the inclusion monotonicity property, i.e.,

$$Y_i(x) \subset Y_j(x) \quad \text{implies} \quad G(x, x', Y_i(x')) \subset G(x, x', Y_j(x'))$$

and if $Y_1(x) \subset Y_0(x)$ for all $x \in [a_0, b_0]$, then from (9-13) it follows by Lemma 8.1 that $Y_{n+1}(x) \subset Y_n(x)$ for all $x \in [a, b]$ and $n = 0, 1, 2, \ldots$.

Since $Y_0(x) = [c, d]$ for all x, we have only to test $Y_1(x) \subset [c, d]$. If by evaluating an interval extension of $Y_1(x)$, say $Y_1(X)$, for $X = [a_0, b_0]$, we have $Y_1([a_0, b_0]) \subset [c, d]$, then we will have $Y_{n+1}(x) \subset Y_n(x)$ for all x in $[a_0, b_0]$ and $n = 0, 1, 2, \ldots$.

If the functions h and G are rational and $a(x), b(x)$ are linear in x and if $h(a_0)$ is in the interior of $[c, d]$, then $Y_1([a_0, b_0])$ *will* be contained in $[c, d]$, for example, if $Y_1(X)$ is a rational interval function and if $b_0 - a_0$ is sufficiently small. Furthermore, if $G([a_0, b_0], [a_0, b_0], [c, d])$ is defined, then there is an $L > 0$ such that [paralleling (9-2)] we have for all $x, x' \in [a_0, b_0]$ and $Y \subset [c, d]$ the relation

$$w(G(x, x', Y)) \le L w(Y) \qquad (9\text{-}14)$$

From (9-13) and (9-14) and (8-12) we find that

$$w(Y_{n+1}(x)) \le L \int_{[a(x), b(x)]} w(Y_n(x')) \, dx' \qquad (9\text{-}15)$$

If $w_n = \max_{x \in [a_0, b_0]} w(Y_n(x))$, we have, from (9-15),

$$w_{n+1} \le L(b_0 - a_0) w_n$$

and therefore, since $Y_0(x) \equiv [c, d]$, we have

$$\max_{x \in [a_0, b_0]} w(Y_n(x)) \le \{L(b_0 - a_0)\}^n (d - c) \qquad (9\text{-}16)$$

From (9-16), we see that for $L(b_0 - a_0) < 1$, the sequence of interval functions defined by (9-13) will converge to a real function satisfying (9-1).

Of course we cannot compute the interval integrals (9-13) exactly; but we can use the methods of Chapter 8 to compute intervals *containing* those defined by the integral in (9-13), and if the intervals we compute are close enough to the ones defined by (9-13) we will still have convergence.

We present next an algorithm for the computation of interval functions containing the solution to (9-1) based on (9-13) and (8-11).

Closely related methods have been proposed by L. B. Rall [4] and

R. W. Brown [2].

Subdivide the interval $[a_0, b_0]$ by points $a_0 = x_0 < x_1 < x_2 < \cdots x_p = b_0$ and call $X_i = [x_{i-1}, x_i]$. For each $n = 1, 2, \ldots$ we will compute a set of intervals $Y_{n,1}, Y_{n,2}, \ldots, Y_{n,p}$ which contain the values of $Y_n(x)$ for x in $X_1, X_2, \ldots, X_p$—that is,

$$Y_n(x) \subset Y_{n,i} \qquad \text{for all } x \in X_i$$

For $n = 0$, we put $Y_{0,i} = [c, d]$ for all i. For $n > 0$, we have the iterative algorithm defining $Y_{n+1,i}$ for each $i = 1, 2, \ldots, p$ by

$$Y_{n+1,i} = H(X_i) + \sum_{X_j \cap A_i \neq \phi} G(X_i, X_j, Y_{n,j})$$

$$\cdot \begin{cases} w(X_j) & \text{if } (i \neq j) \text{ and } X_j \subset A_i; \\ [0, w(X_i \cap A_i)] & \text{if } (X_j \not\subset A_i \text{ or } i = j) \end{cases} \tag{9-17}$$

where

$$A_i = \bigcup_{x \in X_i} [a(x), b(x)]$$

and where $H(X)$ is an interval extension of $h(x)$, and where by $X_j \cap A_i \neq \varnothing$ we mean that the interval sum is taken over values of j for which the intersection of X_j and the interval A_i is *not empty*. We will not concern ourselves particularly with the problem of computing A_i precisely in the most general case. For the two examples (9-10) and (9-12), we have $A_i = [x_0, x_i]$ and $A_i = [x_0, x_1]$, respectively. More generally, the methods of Chapter 6 could be used to find, at least, an interval A_i such that

$$A_i \supset \bigcup_{x \in X_i} [a(x), b(x)]$$

for real rational $a(x), b(x)$. For sharp enough A_i found in this way the result of using (9-17) will be the same regarding containment of the exact solution and will only produce slightly wider intervals than with the precise A_i.

For the intersections $X_j \cap A_i$ we will get $X_j \cap A_i = X_j$ when the intersection is not empty except for two X_j's, one on each end of the interval A_i. One or both of these may consist of a single real number (one of the points x_j of subdivision of $[a_0, b_0]$), in which case, of course, $w(A_i \cap X_j) = 0$.

From the construction of (9-17) and the properties of inclusion monotonicity of rational interval extensions and interval integrals it follows that the intervals $Y_{n+1,i}$ defined by (9-17) will contain $Y_{n+1}(x)$ defined by (9-13) for $x \in X_i$.

Since the points of subdivision $x_1, x_2, \ldots, x_{p-1}$ interior to $[a_0, b_0]$ are common endpoints of two of the X_i's, namely $x_i \in X_i \cap X_{i+1}$, it follows that $Y_{n+1}(x_i)$ defined by (9-13) will satisfy

$$Y_{n+1}(x_i) \subset Y_{n+1,i} \cap Y_{n+1,i+1} \tag{9-18}$$

We will now illustrate the application of (9-17) and (9-18) with an example.

Consider the integral equation

$$y(x) = 1 + \int_{[0,\, x]} y^2(x')\, dx' \qquad (9\text{-}19)$$

Using the notation of (9-1), we have, for (9-19), $h(x) \equiv 1$, $a(x) \equiv 0$, $b(x) = x$, $g(x, x', y(x')) = y^2(x')$.

For $[a_0, b_0]$, we will choose $[a_0, b_0] = [0, \frac{1}{2}]$.

For $[c, d]$ we must choose an interval with $h(x)$ in its interior for all $x \in [a_0, b_0]$; we put $[c, d] = [0, 2]$. For the intervals X_i, we take $X_i = [(i-1)/2p, i/2p]$. Thus $x_i = i/2p$. We put $H(X) \equiv 1$ and $G(X, X', Y) = Y^2$ as the interval extensions of h and g.

For $A_i = \bigcup_{x \in X_i} [a(x), b(x)]$, we have

$$A_i = \bigcup_{x \in X_1} [0, x] = \bigcup_{j=1}^{i} X_j = [0, x_i] \qquad (9\text{-}20)$$

We take, for $n = 0$, $Y_{0,i} \equiv [0, 2]$. Now we are prepared to compute the intervals $Y_{n+1,i}$ from (9-17). For this example, (9-17) becomes

$$Y_{n+1,i} = 1 + \sum_{j=1}^{i-1} Y_{n,j}^2 w(X_j) + Y_{n,i}^2 [0, w(X_i)]$$

or

$$Y_{n+1,i} = 1 + \sum_{j=1}^{i-1} (Y_{n,j}^2)\left(\frac{1}{2p}\right) + Y_{n,i}^2 \left[0, \frac{1}{2p}\right] \qquad (9\text{-}21)$$

The sum $\sum_{j=1}^{i-1}$ in (9-21) is deleted if $i = 1$. For $n = 0$, since $Y_{0,j} = [0, 2]$, $j = 1, 2, \ldots, p$, we have from (9-21)

$$Y_{1,i} = 1 + \sum_{j=1}^{i-1} [0, 4]\frac{1}{2p} + [0, 4]\left[0, \frac{1}{2p}\right]$$

$$= \left[1, 1 + \frac{2i}{p}\right] \qquad (9\text{-}22)$$

In order to have $Y_{1,i} \subset Y_{0,i} = [0, 2]$ we must restrict i to $i \leq p/2$. For $n = 1$, we find

$$Y_{2,i} = 1 + \frac{1}{2p}\sum_{j=1}^{i-1}\left[1, 1 + \frac{2j}{p}\right]^2 + \left[1, 1 + \frac{2i}{p}\right]^2\left[0, \frac{1}{2p}\right]$$

$$= \left[1 + \frac{i-1}{2p}, 1 + \frac{i-1}{2p} + \frac{(i-1)i}{p^2}\right.$$

$$\left. + \frac{(i-1)(i)(2i-1)}{3p^3} + \left(1 + \frac{2i}{p}\right)^2\frac{1}{2p}\right] \qquad (9\text{-}23)$$

For large p, we find that the intervals $Y_{1,i}$, $Y_{2,i}$ given by (9-22) and (9-23) become nearly

$$[1, 1 + 4x_i] \quad \text{and} \quad \left[1 + x_i, 1 + x_i + 4x_i^2 + \frac{16}{3}x_i^3\right]$$

respectively. For this example we can, also, explicitly carry out the interval integrations in (9–13) and obtain

$$Y_0(x) = [0, 2]$$

$$Y_1(x) = 1 + \int_{[0, x]} [0, 2]^2 \, dx' = [1, 1 + 4x]$$

$$Y_2(x) = 1 + \int_{[0, x]} [1, 1 + 4x]^2 = \left[1 + x, 1 + x + 4x^2 + \frac{16x^3}{3}\right]$$

$$Y_3(x) = \left[1 + x + x^2 + \frac{x^3}{3}, 1 + x + x^2 + 3x^3 + \frac{14}{x}x^4 + \frac{16}{3}x^5\right.$$

$$\left. + \frac{64}{9}x^6 + \frac{256}{63}x^7\right] \tag{9-24}$$

Each successive iteration produces agreement of the upper and lower bounding real functions to the next higher-degree polynomial.

For this example, the exact solution of (9–19) is

$$y(x) = \frac{1}{1 - x} = 1 + x + x^2 + x^3 + \cdots \tag{9-25}$$

and it can be checked that for $x \in [0, \frac{1}{2}]$ the intervals computed above do contain the solution. For example, for $x \in [0, \frac{1}{2}]$, we have from (9–24), (9–25)

$$Y(x) = 1 + x + x^2 + x^3\left(\frac{1}{1 - x}\right) \in 1 + x + x^2 + x^3[1, 2]$$

$$Y_3(x) = 1 + x + x^2 + x^3\left[\frac{1}{3}, 3 + \frac{14}{3}x + \cdots\right]$$

and therefore $y(x) \in Y_3(x)$ for all $x \in [0, \frac{1}{2}]$.

To illustrate the point of the remark on (9–18), notice from (9–23) that we have

$$Y_{2, i+1} = \left[1 + \frac{i}{2p}, 1 + \frac{i}{2p} + \cdots\right]$$

so, using (9–18),

$$y(x_i) \in Y_2(x_i) = Y_2\left(\frac{i}{2p}\right) \subset \left[1 + \frac{i}{2p}, 1 + \frac{i - 1}{2p} + \frac{(i - 1)i}{p^2} + \cdots\right]$$

and the intersection (9–18) sharpens the bounds for the solution $y(x_i)$ at the points of subdivision $x_1, x_2, x_3, \ldots, x_{p-1}$. For example, if $p = 10, i = 1$ in (9–23), we find that $Y_{2, 1} = [1, 1.072]$, $Y_{2, 2} = [1.05, 1.170]$ and $Y_{2, 1} \cap Y_{2, 2} = [1.05, 1.072]$. The corresponding exact solution is

$$y(x_i) = y\left(\frac{i}{2p}\right) = \frac{1}{1 - .05} = 1.0526\ldots$$

The convergence of the sequence of interval functions defined either by (9–17) or even by (9–13) is very slow and depends on the size of $b_0 - a_0$ and L [see (9–16)]. In the example above, for L we find that for $Y = [y_1, y_2] \subset [0, 2]$

$$w(G(x, x', Y)) = w([y_1, y_2]^2) = y_2^2 - y_1^2$$

so

$$w(G(x, x', Y)) \leq 4(y_2 - y_1) \tag{9-26}$$

and by (9–14) we can only conclude from (9–26) that we can take $L = 4$. Therefore to make the sequence $\{Y_n(x)\}$ converge, according to (9–16) we should not take $b_0 - a_0$ as large as $\frac{1}{4}$. Thus in (9–24) we should restrict x to lie in some interval $[0, t]$ with $t < \frac{1}{4}$; and in (9–21) we should only allow i to vary over $i = 1, 2, \ldots, i_1 < p/2$. Better still, the choice of $[a_0, b_0]$ for the example should have been made so that $b_0 - a_0 < \frac{1}{4}$ in the first place. From our example it is clear that there is not much point in using a more sophisticated approximation to the interval integrals in (9–13) [for example, we might attempt to use (8–15)]. In our example we have seen that even the exact evaluation of the interval integral in (9–13) as shown in (9–24) produces a slowly convergent procedure, *except for very small* $b_0 - a_0$.

For the special type of integral equation (9–10) arising from the initial-value problem (9–9) the procedure described by (9–17) might be useful in a step-by-step fashion over small intervals in x to iteratively narrow down intervals containing the solution. On the other hand, as we shall see in a later chapter, even this use of (9–17) is of limited value for *systems* of equations of the form (9–9).

Nearly all of the discussion and equations of this and the previous section can be carried over with little change to vector functions y, h, g in (9–1).

The method using (9–17) is at least *a* way of programming the machine computation (with *rounded*-interval arithmetic evaluation) of intervals containing values of the exact solution to an integral equation (under certain conditions which amount essentially to dealing with domains over which the functions involved have small enough total variation). For the present, we must be content to hope that the discovery of more efficient interval methods for integral equations will be the object of some future investigation.

REFERENCES

1. ANSELONE, P., *Nonlinear Integral Equations*. Madison: The University of Wisconsin Press, 1964.
2. BROWN, R. W., "Upper and lower bounds for solutions of integral equations," in L. B. Rall, ed., *Error in Digital Computation*, Vol. II, pp. 219-230. New York: John Wiley & Sons, Inc., 1965.
3. COLLATZ, L., *The Numerical Treatment of Differential Equations*, 3rd ed., esp. pp. 327-357. Berlin: Springer-Verlag, 1959.
4. RALL, L. B., "Numerical integration and the solution of integral equations by the use of Riemann sums," *SIAM Review*, 7: 1 (January 1965), 55-64.

See especially reference 1 for additional references on methods for approximating solutions to integral equations.

10

THE INITIAL-VALUE PROBLEM IN ORDINARY DIFFERENTIAL EQUATIONS

10.1 INTRODUCTION

In this chapter we consider some interval methods for the initial-value problem in ordinary differential equations.

Under very general conditions an ordinary differential equation of any finite *order* or a system of differential equations of various finite orders can be put into the form of an *autonomous system of first-order equations*

$$\frac{dy_i(x)}{dx} = f_i(y_1(x), \ldots, y_n(x)), \qquad i = 1, 2, \ldots, n \qquad (10\text{--}1)$$

For example, the equation of mth order

$$\frac{d^m y(x)}{dx^m} = g\left(x, y(x), \frac{dy(x)}{dx}, \ldots, \frac{d^{m-1} y(x)}{dx^{m-1}}\right) \qquad (10\text{--}2)$$

can be put into the form (10–1) by making the substitutions

$$x = y_1(x)$$
$$y(x) = y_2(x)$$
$$\frac{dy(x)}{dx} = y_3(x) \qquad (10\text{--}3)$$
$$\vdots$$
$$\frac{d^{m-1} y(x)}{dx^{m-1}} = y_{m+1}(x)$$

in (10–2), which becomes

$$\frac{dy_{m+1}(x)}{dx} = g(y_1(x), y_2(x), \ldots, y_{m+1}(x)) \qquad (10\text{--}4)$$

Putting (10–3) and (10–4) together, we obtain the following system in the form of (10–1) which is equivalent to (10–2):

$$\frac{dy_1(x)}{dx} = 1$$

$$\frac{dy_2(x)}{dx} = y_3(x)$$

$$\vdots$$

$$\frac{dy_m(x)}{dx} = y_{m+1}(x)$$

$$\frac{dy_{m+1}(x)}{dx} = g(y_1(x), y_2(x), \ldots, y_{m+1}(x))$$

Using vector notation, we can abbreviate (10–1) to

$$\frac{dy(x)}{dx} = f(y(x)) \tag{10-5}$$

A vector function $f: E^n \to E^n$ on Euclidean n-dimensional vector space E^n is said to define a *vector field* on E^n. The space E^n is called the *phase space* of the vector differential equation (10–5). In some circumstances one may wish to consider a function f defined on a subset S of E^n; then for $f: S(\subset E^n) \to E^n$, the set S will be the phase space of the differential equation (10–5).

Under certain conditions on the function f, the vector differential equation (10–5) is said to define a *flow* or a *dynamical system* on the phase space S. Through each point y_0 in S there passes a unique solution $y(x, y_0)$ lying in S, with $y(0, y_0) = y_0$.

We will use the metric on the vector space E^n defined by the vector norm

$$|y| = \max_{i=1,2,\ldots,n} |y_i|$$

where $y_1, y_2, \ldots, y_n$ are the components of $y \in E^n$. Thus for the distance between two points y, z in E^n we have

$$|y - z| = \max_{i=1,2,\ldots,n} |y_i - z_i|$$

If f is defined on an n-dimensional rectangle $A = A_1 \otimes A_2 \otimes \cdots \otimes A_n$ where each A_i is a nondegenerate interval $A_i = [a_i, b_i]$, $b_i > a_i$, and if there is a positive real number L such that for all points u, v in A, f satisfies the Lipschitz condition

$$|f(u) - f(v)| \le L|u - v| \tag{10-6}$$

then through every point y_0 in the interior of A there passes a unique curve (or an "arc" of a curve) which can be represented as $y(x)$ with $y(x)$ satisfying (10–5) for x in some interval $[-a_0, a_0]$, $a_0 > 0$, and $y(0) = y_0$.

The number a_0 depends on the point y_0. For proofs and discussion of this standard existence and uniqueness theorem we refer the reader to works on ordinary differential equations.

In the next section we prove an interval version of this existence theorem and at the same time derive a "first-order" method for the machine computation of intervals containing exact values of the solution $y(x)$ to the *initial-value problem*, consisting of seeking a function y satisfying (10–5) for some interval of values of x and such that at $x = 0$, the function has a prescribed (vector) value $y(0) = y_0$.

In a subsequent section we discuss the application of Taylor series expansions with interval remainder terms to the derivation of Kth-order interval methods for the initial-value problem. The application is similar to the use made of Taylor series in Section 8.2.

In Chapter 11 we will discuss the machine generation of the Taylor coefficients required by our Kth-order methods.

10.2 A FIRST-ORDER INTERVAL METHOD

Given a (vector) differential equation of the form (10–15) with f defined on $A = A_1 \otimes A_2 \otimes \cdots \otimes A_n$, $A_i = [a_i, b_i]$, $b_i > a_i$, and a point y_0 in the interior of A, $a_i < (y_0)_i < b_i$, $i = 1, 2, \ldots, n$, suppose we have interval extensions F_i of the real functions f_i (which are the components of the vector function f) with the following properties for $i = 1, 2, \ldots, n$:

(1) $F_i(Y_1, Y_2, \ldots, Y_n)$ is defined and continuous for $Y_j \subset A_j, j = 1, 2, \ldots, n$.

(2) F_i is inclusion monotonic, i.e., $Y_1' \subset Y_1, \ldots, Y_n' \subset Y_n$ implies

$$F_i(Y_1', Y_2', \ldots, Y_n') \subset F_i(Y_1, Y_2, \ldots, Y_n)$$

for $Y_j \subset A_j, j = 1, 2, \ldots, n$.

(3) There is a positive real number L such that for all $Y_j \subset A_j, j = 1, 2, \ldots, n$, we have

$$w(F_i(Y_1, Y_2, \ldots, Y_n)) \leq L \max_{j=1,2,\ldots,n} w(Y_j)$$

For a set of rational interval functions F_i with

$$F_i(y_1, y_2, \ldots, y_n) = f_i(y_1, y_2, \ldots, y_n)$$

for $y_j \in A_j, j = 1, 2, \ldots, n$, the properties (1), (2), and (3) will be satisfied if $F_i(A_1, A_2, \ldots, A_n)$ is defined for $i = 1, 2, \ldots, n$. And this *will* be the case if, using rounded-interval arithmetic, we can evaluate the expressions $F_i(Y_1, Y_2, \ldots, Y_n)$ for $Y_j = A_j$ for all $i = 1, 2, \ldots, n$.

Using interval-vector notation, we can write the conditions (1), (2), (3) as follows:

(1') $F(Y)$ is defined and continuous for $Y \subset A$.

(2′) F is inclusion monotonic, i.e., $Y' \subset Y$ implies $F(Y') \subset F(Y)$.

(3′) There is an $L > 0$ such that for all $Y \subset A$, we have $w(F(Y)) \leq Lw(Y)$.

Suppose now that we have an interval-vector function F which satisfies (1′), (2′), (3′) and suppose that y_0 is the *interior* of A. Then there is a positive h such that for $x \in [0, h]$,

$$y_0 + xF(A) \subset A \qquad (10\text{--}7)$$

In component form (10–7) states that for each i,

$$(y_0)_i + xF_i(A_1, A_2, \ldots, A_n) \subset A_i \qquad (10\text{--}8)$$

For each $i = 1, 2, \ldots, n$, (10–8) will be satisfied for $x \in [0, h_i]$ for some positive h_i; then for h we can take the minimum of these h_i, $i = 1, 2, \ldots, n$.

PROBLEM 10.1. Describe a procedure for finding each h_i.

Let p be a positive integer and subdivide the interval $[0, h]$ into subintervals

$$X_s = \left[\frac{s-1}{p}h, \frac{s}{p}h \right], \qquad s = 1, 2, \ldots, p$$

For each positive integer p, we define an interval-vector-valued function $Y_{(p)}(x)$ for $x \in [0, h]$ as follows:

$$Y_{(p)}(0) = y_0$$

For $x_s = (s/p)h, s = 1, 2, \ldots, p$, put

$$Y_{(p)}(x_s) = Y_{(p)}(x_{s-1}) + \frac{h}{p}F(S_s) \qquad (10\text{--}9)$$

where

$$S_s = Y_{(p)}(x_{s-1}) + \left[0, \frac{h}{p} \right]F(A) \qquad (10\text{--}10)$$

For $x_{s-1} < x < x_s$, put

$$Y_{(p)}(x) = Y_{(p)}(x_{s-1}) + (x - x_{s-1})F(S_s) \qquad (10\text{--}11)$$

Notice that $x_s - x_{s-1} = h/p$ and therefore the equations (10–9), (10–10), (10–11) together with $Y_{(p)}(0) = Y_0$ define a piecewise-linear-in-x, continuous, interval-vector-valued function $Y_{(p)}(x)$ for all $x \in [0, h]$.

We have the following result.

THEOREM 10.1. The initial-value problem (10–5) with $y(0) = y_0$, where f is the real restriction of an interval-vector function F satisfying (1′), (2′), (3′), has a unique solution $y(x)$ for $x \in [0, h]$, h defined by (10–7), and $y(x) \in Y_{(p)}(x)$ for all $p = 1, 2, \ldots$ and, furthermore, there is an $L_1 > 0$ such that for all $x \in [0, h]$,

$$w(Y_{(p)}(x)) \leq L_1\left(\frac{1}{p}\right) \tag{10-12}$$

Proof. We prove the theorem by showing that

$$\bigcap_{p=1}^{\infty} Y_{(p)}(x)$$

defines a real vector function $y(x)$ which satisfies (10–5). The uniqueness follows from property (3'). We show the inequality (10–12) first.

From (10–11) we have

$$w(Y_{(p)}(x)) \leq w(Y_{(p)}(x_{s-1})) + (x - x_{s-1})w(F(S_s)) \tag{10-13}$$

Using property (3') and (10–10), we have

$$w(F(S_s)) \leq L\{w(Y_{(p)}(x_{s-1})) + \frac{h}{p}(3|F(A)|)\} \tag{10-14}$$

Here we have used the fact that for any two intervals I, J it follows that

$$w(IJ) \leq |I|w(J) + |J|w(I) \quad \text{and} \quad w(I) \leq 2|I|$$

Putting (10–13) and (10–14) together and using induction on s, we find for $x \in [0, h]$ that

$$w(Y_{(p)}(x)) \leq \left\{1 + \left(1 + \frac{hL}{p}\right) + \left(1 + \frac{hL}{p}\right)^2 + \cdots \right.$$

$$\left. + \left(1 + \frac{hL}{p}\right)^{p-1}\right\}\frac{3Lh^2}{p^2}|F(A)|$$

$$\leq \frac{\left(1 + \frac{hL}{p}\right)^p - 1}{\left(1 + \frac{hL}{p}\right) - 1}\frac{3Lh^2}{p^2}|F(A)|$$

Since $(1 + hL/p)^p < e^{hL}$, we have

$$w(Y_{(p)}(x)) \leq \frac{3|F(A)|(e^{hL} - 1)h}{p} \tag{10-15}$$

which yields (10–12).

In order to show that $\bigcap_{p=1}^{\infty} Y_{(p)}(x)$ is nonempty we invoke the "finite intersection property" characterization of compact sets.* We show that $Y_{(p)}(x) \subset A$ for $p = 1, 2, \ldots$ and all $x \in [0, h]$ and that the intersection $Y_{(p_1)}(x) \cap Y_{(p_2)}(x)$ is nonempty for any pair of integers $p_1, p_2 \geq 1$. The family of closed intervals $\{Y_{(p)}(x)\}_{p=1,2,\ldots}$ has the finite intersection property, i.e., the intersection of any finite collection of members is nonempty. Since A is compact, it follows that $\bigcap_{p=1}^{\infty} Y_{(p)}(x)$ is nonempty.

---

*See J. L. Kelley, *General Topology* (Princeton, N.J.: D. Van Nostrand Co., Inc., 1955), pp. 135–136.

From the definition of h by (10–7) and by an inductive argument it follows from (10–9), (10–10), (10–11) that $S_s \subset A$ for all $s = 1, 2, \ldots, p$ and that $Y_{(p)}(x) \subset A$ for all $x \in [0, h]$. Furthermore, by a similar argument it follows that $x \in [0, h]$ implies

$$Y_{(mp)}(x) \subset Y_{(p)}(x)$$

for any positive integer m.

Given two integers $p_1, p_2 \geq 1$, it then follows that

$$Y_{(p_1 p_2)}(x) \subset Y_{(p_1)}(x) \quad \text{and} \quad Y_{(p_1 p_2)}(x) \subset Y_{(p_2)}(x)$$

Since $Y_{(p)}(x)$ is clearly itself nonempty for all $p \geq 1$, it follows that the intersection $Y_{(p_1)}(x) \cap Y_{(p_2)}(x)$ which contains $Y_{(p_1 p_2)}(x)$ is also nonempty.

We have shown that $\bigcap\limits_{p=1}^{\infty} Y_{(p)}(x)$ is nonempty, and from (10–15) it follows that $\bigcap\limits_{p=1}^{\infty} Y_{(p)}(x)$ has width zero for $x \in [0, h]$ and therefore defines a real function

$$y(x) = \bigcap_{p=1}^{\infty} Y_{(p)}(x)$$

To show that $y(x)$ satisfies (10–5) we argue that from property (1'), i.e., the continuity of $F(Y)$, it follows that each $Y_{(p)}(x)$ is continuous; and by Lemma 8.1, since $y(x) \in Y_{(p)}(x)$, and $f(y) \in F(y)$, it follows that

$$\int_{[0,x]} f(y(x'))\, dx' \in \int_{[0,x]} F(Y_{(p)}(x'))\, dx' \tag{10–16}$$

Since from (10–10) and (10–11) it follows that $Y_{(p)}(x) \subset S_s$ for $x \in [x_{s-1}, x_s]$, we have by (8–11) and (10–11) that

$$y_0 + \int_{[0,x]} F(Y_{(p)}(x'))\, dx' \subset Y_{(p)}(x) \tag{10–17}$$

From (10–16) and (10–17) we find that

$$y_0 + \int_{[0,x]} f(y(x'))\, dx' \in Y_{(p)}(x)$$

for $p = 1, 2, \ldots$, and therefore

$$y_0 + \int_{[0,x]} f(y(x'))\, dx' = y(x) = \bigcap_{p=1}^{\infty} Y_{(p)}(x) \tag{10–18}$$

The equation

$$y(x) = y_0 + \int_{[0,x]} f(y(x'))\, dx'$$

implies that y satisfies (10–5). [The required continuity of $y(x)$ follows from the compactness of $[0, h]$ and the continuity of the functions $Y_{(p)}(x)$.]

Suppose we had two solutions $y_1(x), y_2(x)$; then, by (10–18),

$$\int_{[0,x]} (f(y_1(x')) - f(y_2(x')))\, dx' = y_1(x) - y_2(x) \tag{10–19}$$

But condition (3′) implies that $|f(y_1) - f(y_2)| \leq L|y_1 - y_2|$ and (10–19) is impossible for $y_1(x) \neq y_2(x)$ if $xL < 1$. By repeated application in steps of $1/L$ we get uniqueness for $x \in [0, h]$.

This completes the proof of Theorem 10.1.

In order to *continue* an "interval solution" $Y_{(p)}(x)$ beyond $x = h$, we can proceed as follows:

Having computed $Y_{(p)}(h)$, we may be able to find an interval vector B such that $Y_{(p)}(h)$ is in the interior of B and such that $F(B)$ is defined (i.e., can be evaluated as an interval vector). In that case we can determine a new h from (10–7), replacing y_0 by $Y_{(p)}(h)$ as our new "initial value" and replacing A by B. The formulas (10–9), (10–10), (10–11) can now be applied over the new interval of values of x.

For the inequality (10–15) in the proof of Theorem 10.1, we obtain in the more general case of $w(y_0) \geq 0$,

$$w(Y_{(p)}(x)) \leq \frac{3|F(A)|(e^{hL} - 1)h}{p} + e^{hL}w(y_0) \qquad (10\text{–}20)$$

Thus, in our continuation procedure, as long as we have $w(y_0) \leq L_2/p$ for some $L_2 > 0$ which is independent of p, then (10–12) will still be true. Therefore, we can continue our interval solution $Y_{(p)}(x)$ over successive intervals $[0, h^{(1)}], h^{(1)} + [0, h^{(2)}], h^{(1)} + h^{(2)} + [0, h^{(3)}], \ldots$ as long as we can keep on finding interval vectors $A^{(1)}, A^{(2)}, \ldots$ such that

$$Y_{(p)}\left(\sum_{r'=1}^{r} h^{(r')} \right) \qquad \text{is interior to } A^{(r+1)}$$

and $F(A^{(r+1)})$ can be computed as an interval vector.

The formulas (10–7), (10–9), (10–10), (10–11), together with the continuation procedure described above, define our *first-order method* for interval solutions of initial-value problems. We can also apply the method in case the initial value y_0 is a nondegenerate interval vector, $w(y_0) > 0$. In this case the interval solutions $Y_{(p)}(x)$ will contain the real solution $y(x)$ passing through each real vector initial value in y_0. And also in this case the bound on $w(Y_{(p)}(x))$ given in Theorem 10.1, which assumes $w(y_0) = 0$, can be replaced by

$$w(Y_{(p)})(x)) \leq \frac{L_1}{p} + L_2 w(y_0)$$

for some L_1, L_2 independent of p (but depending on the range of values of x).

Notice that the interval solutions $Y_{(p)}(x)$ given by this first-order method contain the exact solution for *all* values of x in the intervals $[0, h^{(1)}], [h^{(1)}, h^{(2)}], \ldots$. In between the points of subdivision x_s, the formula (10–11) defines the value of $Y_{(p)}(x)$ containing the exact solution value $y(x)$.

We conclude this section with an example illustrating the application of the first-order method.

Consider the single differential equation of first order

$$\frac{dy(x)}{dx} = y^2(x) \tag{10-21}$$

with the initial value $y(0) = 1$.

For our interval extension of the function $f(y) = y^2$ we take $F(Y) = Y^2$. For the interval A in (10–7) we take $A = [0, 2]$. Then $y_0 = 1$ is interior to A, and (10–7) becomes (since $F(A) = A^2 = [0, 4]$) for $x \in [0, h]$

$$1 + x[0, 4] \subset [0, 2] \tag{10-22}$$

From (10–22), chose $h = \frac{1}{4}$. Then x_s becomes $x_s = s/4p$ and (10–9), (10–10), (10–11) become

$$Y_{(p)}(x_s) = Y_{(p)}(x_{s-1}) + \frac{1}{4p}S_s^2 \tag{10-23}$$

$$S_s = Y_{(p)}(x_{s-1}) + \left[0, \frac{1}{4p}\right][0, 4]$$

$$= Y_{(p)}(x_{s-1}) + \left[0, \frac{1}{p}\right] \tag{10-24}$$

and, for $x \in [x_{s-1}, x_s]$,

$$Y_{(p)}(x) = Y_{(p)}(x_{s-1}) + (x - x_{s-1})S_s^2 \tag{10-25}$$

In Fig. 10.1 the geometrical significance of the various quantities in these equations is shown for $p = 2$. The x-scale is enlarged for clarity.

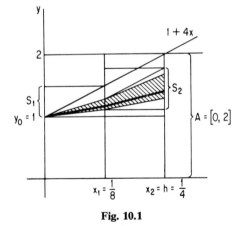

Fig. 10.1

Thus h is seen to have been determined as the value of x at which the lines $y = 2$ and $y = 1 + 4x$ intersect. We have $x_1 = h/p = \frac{1}{8}$ for $p = 2$ and $h = \frac{1}{4}$; and $x_2 = 2h/p = \frac{1}{4}$. For S_1, we find $S_1 = 1 + [0, \frac{1}{2}] = [1, 1\frac{1}{2}]$; and $Y_{(2)}(x) = 1 + x[1, \frac{9}{4}]$ for $x \in [0, \frac{1}{8}]$, so that

$$Y_{(2)}(x_1) = 1 + [\tfrac{4}{32}, \tfrac{9}{32}]$$

Finally,

$$S_2 = 1 + [\tfrac{4}{32}, \tfrac{9}{32}] + [0, \tfrac{1}{2}] = [\tfrac{36}{32}, \tfrac{57}{32}]$$

and

$$Y_{(2)}(x) = 1 + [\tfrac{4}{32}, \tfrac{9}{32}] + (x - \tfrac{1}{8})[\tfrac{1296}{1024}, \tfrac{3249}{1024}]$$

for $x \in [\tfrac{1}{8}, \tfrac{1}{4}]$, so that

$$Y_{(2)}(x_2) \subset [1.28, 1.69]$$

using three-decimal rounded-interval arithmetic. The shaded region in the figure indicates the interval solution $Y_{(2)}(x)$. The exact solution $y(x) = 1/(1 - x)$ is indicated by the heavy curve interior to the shaded region.

For the example at hand, (10–21), the inequality (10–20) can be made more precise as follows. For L, we can put $L = 2|A|$, since

$$w(F([y_1, y_2])) = w([y_1^2, y_2^2])$$

and

$$w([y_1^2, y_2^2]) = (y_2 - y_1)(y_1 + y_2) \le 2|A| w([y_1, y_2])$$

for $y_1, y_2 \in A$.

Call our first h and A, $h^{(1)} = \tfrac{1}{4}$, $A^{(1)} = [0, 2]$; then we had $Y_{(p)}(0) + h^{(1)}(A^{(1)})^2 = A^{(1)}$. From (10–20) we find that $w(Y_{(p)}(h^{(1)})) \le 3(e - 1)/p$. Call

$$x^{(r)} = \sum_{r'=1}^{r} h^{(r')}$$

for subsequent intervals $[h^{(1)}, h^{(1)} + h^{(2)}]$ in our continuation procedure. Then $A^{(r+1)}$ and $h^{(r+1)}$ can be chosen so that

$$Y_{(p)}(x^{(r)}) + h^{(r+1)}(A^{(r+1)})^2 \subset A^{(r+1)} \qquad (10\text{–}26)$$

Since $w(Y_{(p)}(x^{(r)}))$ can be made arbitrarily small for large enough p, and since the exact solution is $y(x) = 1/(1 - x)$, if we choose $A^{(r+1)} = Y_{(p)}(x^{(r)}) + [-1, 1]$, then $h^{(r+1)}$ will be chosen, from (10–26), almost as large as

$$\left(\frac{1 - x^{(r)}}{2 - x^{(r)}}\right)^2$$

In particular, we may suppose that $A^{(r+1)}$ is chosen so that $h^{(r+1)} \ge (1 - x^{(r)})^2/4$ and $h^{(r+1)}|A^{(r+1)}|^2 \le 1$. Then we have

$$h^{(r)}|A^{(r)}| \le \frac{1}{|A^{(r)}|} = \frac{1}{|1/(1 - x^{(r)}) + 1|} \le \frac{1}{2}$$

From (10–20) we have in this case

$$w(Y_{(p)}(x^{(r)})) \le \frac{3|A^{(r)}|^2(e^{2h^{(r)}|A^{(r)}|} - 1)h^{(r)}}{p}$$
$$+ e^{2h^{(r)}|A^{(r)}|} w(Y_{(p)}(x^{(r-1)}))$$

$$\leq \frac{3(e-1)}{p} + ew(Y_{(p)}(x^{(r-1)}))$$

$$\leq \frac{3(e-1)}{p}(1 + e + e^2 + \cdots + e^{r-1})$$

or

$$w(Y_{(p)}(x^{(r)})) < \frac{3(e^r - 1)}{p} \qquad (10\text{--}27)$$

Furthermore, since $h^{(r+1)} \geq (1 - x^{(r)})^2/4$ and $x^{(r)} = x^{(r-1)} + h$, with $x^{(0)} = 0$, it follows that

$$0 = x^{(0)} < x^{(1)} < x^{(2)} < \cdots < x^{(r-1)} < x^{(r)} < \cdots < 1$$

The $x^{(r)}$ *cannot* be ≥ 1 since $y(x) = 1/(1 - x) \in Y_{(p)}(x)$ for $x \in [0, x^{(r)}]$ and the $x^{(r)}$ are *chosen* so that $Y_{(p)}(x)$ can be computed as an interval (i.e., a closed, *bounded* real interval) for *all* $x \in [0, x^{(r)}]$. The $x^{(r)}$ cannot have a a limit < 1 either, since then $h^{(r+1)} \geq (1 - x^{(r)})^2/4$ would imply that $h^{(r)}$ had a positive lower bound and the sequence of $x^{(r)}$'s would be unbounded, which contradicts $x^{(r)} < 1$.

Thus we have shown that for the example (10–21) the first-order interval method can be continued, for arbitrarily small $\delta > 0$, to within δ of 1, i.e., we can eventually reach $Y_{(p)}(x^{(r)})$ for $x^{(r)} > 1 - \delta$. For sufficiently large p, the first value of r for which $x^{(r)} > 1 - \delta$ will not increase with with increasing p; therefore, from (10–27), for sufficiently large p we can make $w(Y_{(p)}(x))$ arbitrarily small for all $x \in [0, 1 - \delta]$.

This will still be true if we carry out the evaluation of (10–9) and (10–10) in rounded-interval arithmetic on the computer, provided sufficiently high precision is used in the rounded-interval arithmetic subroutines. For evaluations of $Y_{(p)}(x_s)$ using a *given* fixed precision in the rounded-interval arithmetic we will still obtain interval solutions $Y_{(p)}(x)$ which contain the exact solution $y(x)$, but the width of $Y_{(p)}(x)$ will now depend on the (multiple) word length used as well as on p, and $w(Y_{(p)}(x))$ will no longer converge to zero as p goes to infinity.

The width of $Y_{(p)}(x)$ will also depend on the choice of the interval vector A used in (10–7) and (10–10). Given an initial-value problem, the computer can be programmed to find an appropriate A. In fact, various general schemes for choosing A and p can be programmed so that the machine can carry out all the steps required for applying the first-order method given only the differential equations and initial values. We will discuss such a scheme in the next section in connection with the more useful "Kth-order" methods.

PROBLEM 10.2. Using three-decimal rounded-interval arithmetic with the first-order method, determine $Y_{(p)}(x)$ for the initial-value problem (10–21),

$y(0) = 1$; setting $p = 2$ and $A = [.900; 1.18]$, find $Y_{(p)}(x)$ for $x \in [0, h]$ with h determined from (10-7).

PROBLEM 10.3. Use the methods of Section 9.2 to improve the interval solution obtained in problem 10.2.

PROBLEM 10.4. Using Theorem 10-1, show that the initial-value problem defined by

$$\frac{dy(x)}{dx} = \frac{1}{x^2 + y^2}$$

with $y(0) = 2$ has a unique solution $y(x)$ for *all* real x.

10.3 A Kth-ORDER INTERVAL METHOD

The vector differential equation (10–5) is written in component form as (10–1). Throughout this section we will assume the functions $f_i(y) = f_i(y_1, y_2, \ldots, y_n)$, $i = 1, 2, \ldots, n$, have continuous total derivatives of all orders with respect to x along solutions to (10–5) at all points in some open set in E^n containing the *initial* point (or initial interval vector) y_0. That is, we define

$$f_i^{(j)}(y_1(x), \ldots, y_n(x))$$

recursively by

$$f_i^{(0)}(y_1(x), \ldots, y_n(x)) = f_i(y_1(x), \ldots, y_n(x))$$

and for $j = 1, 2, \ldots$, denoting $f_i^{(j)}(y_1(x), \ldots, y_n(x))$ by $f_i^{(j)}$, by

$$f_i^{(j)} = \sum_{m=1}^{n} \frac{\partial f_i^{(j-1)}}{\partial y_m} f_m^{(0)} \tag{10-28}$$

From (10–1) we have for $j = 1, 2, \ldots$

$$\frac{d^j y_i(x)}{dx^j} = f_i^{(j-1)}(y_1(x), \ldots, y_n(x)) \tag{10-29}$$

In the next chapter we will describe a method for programming the computer to generate the functions $f_i^{(j)}$ and interval extensions $F_i^{(j)}$ from a description of the functions f_i in a given initial-value problem for a system of the form (10–1), for a fairly general class of functions f_i including rational functions.

We also suppose, in this section, that the functions $f_i^{(j)}$ have interval extensions $F_i^{(j)}$ defined and continuous for Y in some n-dimensional rectangle A containing y_0, and that $Y' \subset Y \subset A$ implies

$$F_i^{(j)}(Y') \subset F_i^{(j)}(Y) \tag{10-30}$$

Furthermore we assume that for each $j = 0, 1, 2, \ldots$ there is an $L_j > 0$ such that for $Y \subset A$ we have

$$w(F^{(j)}(Y)) \leq L_j w(Y) \tag{10-31}$$

By $F^{(j)}(Y)$ we mean, of course, the interval-vector-valued function with components $F^{(j)}(Y) = (F_1^{(j)}(Y), \ldots, F_n^{(j)}(Y))$.

If the functions $y_1(x), \ldots, y_n(x)$ have continuous derivatives of all orders for $x \in [0, h]$ satisfying (10-29), then the Taylor theorem with remainder asserts that for $x \in [0, h]$, $K > 1$,

$$y_i(x) = y_i(0) + \sum_{j=1}^{K-1} \frac{f_i^{(j-1)}(y_1(0), \ldots, y_n(0))}{j!} x^j + \frac{f_i^{(K-1)}(y_1(\theta), \ldots, y_n(\theta))}{K!} x^K$$

for some $\theta \in [0, x]$.

If the interval extensions $F_i^{(j)}$ are defined for the interval vector A, and $y(0) \in Y(0) \subset A$, then $y_i(x) \in Y_i(x)$ where

$$Y_i(x) = Y_i(0) + \sum_{j=1}^{K-1} \frac{F_i^{(j-1)}(Y(0))}{j!} x^j + \frac{F_i^{(K-1)}(A)}{K!} x^K \tag{10-32}$$

provided that $Y([0, h]) \subset A$.

From (10-31) and (10-32) we have, for $x \in [0, h]$,

$$w(Y(x)) \leq \frac{L_{K-1}}{K!} w(A) h^K + \left\{ 1 + \sum_{j=1}^{K-1} \frac{L_{j-1}}{j!} h^j \right\} w(Y(0)) \tag{10-33}$$

Rather than subdivide the interval $[0, h]$ as we did for our first-order method in Section 10.2, we will proceed in another way with the application of (10-32). We will try to choose an h and an A so that $w(Y(x))$ from (10-32) is "as small as possible for as long as possible."

If $w(Y(0)) = 0$, then from (10-32)

$$w(Y(x)) = \frac{w(F^{(K-1)}(A))}{K!} x^K \tag{10-34}$$

In this case, for a given h, we can make $w(Y(x))$ small, for all $x \in [0, h]$, by choosing A such that $w(A)$ is small, since $w(F^{(K-1)}(A)) \leq L_{K-1} w(A)$. On the other hand, we cannot make $w(A)$ smaller than the width of the narrowest A for which $Y([0, h]) \subset A$, otherwise we cannot guarantee $y(x) \in Y(x)$. Therefore we must, at least, have

$$w(A) \geq w(Y([0, h])) \geq |F^{(0)}(Y(0))| h \tag{10-35}$$

Now for an autonomous system (10-1) either we will have $|f(y_0)| \neq 0$ or else the point y_0 is a so-called "rest point," i.e., $y(x) \equiv y_0$ for all x, if $y(0) = y_0$.

If it should happen that $w(F^{(K-1)}(A)) = 0$ for an $A = (A_1, A_2, \ldots, A_n)$ such that $w(A_i) > 0$ for $i = 1, 2, \ldots, n$, then it must be the case that $d^K y(x)/dx^K = \text{constant}$ for $x \in [0, h]$ and therefore that the solution $y(x)$ to the initial-value problem (10-5) with $y(0) = y_0$ is a polynomial of degree K in x for $x \in [0, h]$, with $y_0 \in A$ and $Y([0, h]) \subset A$. This follows from the fact that if $d^K y(x)/dx^K$ is *not* constant, then, from (10-29), the functions

$f_i^{(K-1)}$ will not all be constant and some $F_i^{(K-1)}(A)$ will have positive width. From (10–34) we can make $w(Y(x))$ *small* relative to $|Y(x)|$ for $x \in [0, h]$ if we make

$$\frac{w(F^{(K-1)}(A))}{K!} h^K \quad \text{small}$$

relative to $|Y(x)|$. From (10–35) and (10–32), since we require that $Y([0, h]) \subset A$, we will estimate $|Y(x)|$ by $\max(|y_0|, x|F^{(0)}(y_0)|)$ and we estimate $|Y([0, h])|$ by

$$M_0 = \max(|y_0|, h|F^{(0)}(y_0)|) \tag{10–36}$$

We will, further, estimate $w(F^{(K-1)}(A))$ by $|F^{(K)}(y_0)|h$, based on (10–29), the mean-value theorem, and the supposition that we are going to take nearly the narrowest A satisfying $Y([0, h]) \subset A$.

Using these estimates, we put

$$\frac{|F^{(K)}(y_0)|h}{K!} h^K = \epsilon M \tag{10–37}$$

in order to choose an h which will make

$$\max_{x \in [0,h]} w(Y(x)) \approx \epsilon \max_{x \in [0,h]} |Y(x)|$$

From (10–37) we choose

$$h = \left(\frac{\epsilon |y_0|}{|F^{(K)}(y_0)/K!|} \right)^{1/(K+1)} \quad \text{if} \ \left(\frac{\epsilon |y_0|}{|F^{(K)}(y_0)/K!|} \right)^{1/(K+1)} < \frac{|y_0|}{|F^{(0)}(y_0)|}$$

or $\tag{10–38}$

$$h = \left(\frac{\epsilon |F^{(0)}(y_0)|}{|F^{(K)}(y_0)/K!|} \right)^{1/K} \quad \text{otherwise}$$

Using h from (10–38), we put

$$A^{(0)} = y_0 + F^{(0)}(y_0)[0, h] \tag{10–39}$$

and test $Y([0, h]) \subset A^{(0)}$, using (10–32). We proceed as follows:

(1) If $Y([0, h]) \subset A^{(0)}$, then we put $A^{(1)} = Y([0, h])$ and compute

$$\frac{F^{(K-1)}(A^{(1)})}{K!} \subset \frac{F^{(K-1)}(A^{(0)})}{K!}$$

We take as our interval solution in $[0, h]$ the interval-vector function

$$Y(x) = y_0 + \sum_{j=1}^{K-1} \frac{F^{(j-1)}(y_0)}{j!} x^j + \frac{F^{(K-1)}(A^{(1)})}{K!} x^K \tag{10–40}$$

(2) If $Y([0, h]) \not\subset A^{(0)}$, then we put $A^{(1)} = Y([0, h])$ and compute $Y([0, h])$ from (10–40).

(3) If $Y([0, h])$ as computed in (2) is contained in $A^{(1)}$, we take (10–40) as our interval solution for $x \in [0, h]$; otherwise we *alternately* replace h by $h/2$ and replace $A^{(r)}$ by $Y([0, h])$, using (10–40) with $A^{(r)}$ instead of $A^{(1)}$, until we reach a pair of quantities h, $A^{(r)}$ such that

$$Y([0, h]) \subset A^{(r)} \qquad (10\text{-}41)$$

Then, using $A^{(r)}$ in (10-40), we obtain an interval solution $Y(x)$ in $[0, h]$. We can expect to reach (10-41) in a finite number of steps $r = 1, 2, \ldots, q$, since the replacement of h by the $h/2$ diminishes the width of the interval vector on the left-hand side of (10-41) and both sides contain the common values

$$y_0 + \sum_{j=1}^{K-1} \frac{F^{(j-1)}(y_0)}{j!} \left[0, \frac{h}{2}\right]^j$$

The entire procedure outlined can be continued with the new initial value $Y(h)$ replacing y_0 (see Appendix 2). We illustrate the Kth-order method with some examples.

For the initial-value problem discussed in Section 10.2,

$$\frac{dy(x)}{dx} = y^2(x), \qquad y(0) = 1$$

we have $f(y) = y^2$, $f^{(1)}(y) = 2yy' = 2y^3$, $f^{(2)}(y) = 3!y^4, \ldots, f^{(j)}(y) = (j + 1)!y^{j+2}$, so we take $F^{(j)}(Y) = (j + 1)!Y^{j+2}$ and (10-38) becomes, for this example, since $y_0 = 1$,

$$h = \left(\frac{\epsilon}{K + 1}\right)^{1/(K+1)} \qquad \text{if} \quad \epsilon < K + 1 \qquad (10\text{-}42)$$

From (10-39), for $A^{(0)}$ we have

$$A^{(0)} = 1 + [0, h] = [1, 1 + h] \qquad (10\text{-}43)$$

and from (10-32), we determine that

$$Y([0, h]) = 1 + \sum_{j=1}^{K-1} [0, h]^j + [1, (1 + h)^{K+1}][0, h]^K$$

$$= [1, 1 + h + h^2 + \cdots + h^{K-1} + h^K(1 + h)^{K+1}] \qquad (10\text{-}44)$$

We can see that $Y([0, h])$ from (10-44) will *not* be contained in $A^{(0)}$.

From step (2) of our procedure for choosing A and h, we put

$$A^{(1)} = [1, 1 + h + h^2 + \cdots + h^K(1 + h)^{K+1}] \qquad (10\text{-}45)$$

and compute $Y([0, h])$ from (10-40). Again we will have $Y([0, h]) \not\subset A^{(1)}$. This time, from step (3) of our procedure, we replace h by $h/2$, leaving $A^{(1)}$ as given by (10-45) in (10-40), and we compute $Y([0, h/2])$ from (10-40) to obtain

$$Y\left(\left[0, \frac{h}{2}\right]\right) = \left[1, 1 + \frac{h}{2} + \cdots + \left(\frac{h}{2}\right)^{K-1}\right.$$

$$\left. + \left(\frac{h}{2}\right)^K \{1 + h + \cdots + h^K(1 + h)^{K+1}\}^{K+1}\right] \qquad (10\text{-}46)$$

and it can be shown that we will have $Y([0, h/2])$ from (10-46) contained in $A^{(1)}$ from (10-45), for example, if $h \leq 2$, or, from (10-42), if

$\epsilon \leq (K + 1)2^{K+1}$. For $\epsilon < K + 1$, certainly, we will have $Y([0, h/2])$ from (10–46) contained in $A^{(1)}$ given by (10–45).

Therefore, for $x \in [0, \frac{1}{2}(\epsilon/(K + 1))^{1/(K+1)}]$, the initial-value problem $y' = y^2, y(0) = 1$, has a solution $y(x)$ contained in the interval function

$$Y(x) = 1 + \sum_{j=1}^{K-1} x^j + (A^{(1)})^{K+1} x^K \qquad (10\text{–}47)$$

with $A^{(1)}$ given by (10–45) and $h = (\epsilon/(K + 1))^{1/(K+1)}$. From (10–47) we find that for $x \in [0, h/2]$

$$w(Y(x)) = x^K((1 + h + h^2 + \cdots + h^{K-1} + h^K(1 + h)^{K+1})^{K+1} - 1) \quad (10\text{–}48)$$

where

$$h = \left(\frac{\epsilon}{K + 1}\right)^{1/(K+1)} \qquad (10\text{–}49)$$

For $\epsilon = 10^{-9}$, $K = 9$, we have $h = (10^{-10})^{1/10} = 0.1$ and, from (10–48), $w(Y(x))$ for $x \in [0, .05]$ satisfies $w(Y(x)) \leq 10^{-11}$. For comparison, consider $\epsilon = 10^{-9}$ and $K = 4$; then $h = .011 \ldots$ and for $x \in [0, .0057 \ldots]$ we have from (10–48), using $K = 4$, $w(Y(x)) \leq 10^{-10}$.

From the comparison of the "steps" we can take with $K = 4$ and $K = 9$ we would expect to have to "continue" the expansions (10–47) using $K = 4$ someting like nine times to reach the value of $x = .05$, which is reached in one expansion using $K = 9$. In this example the amount of computation per step using (10–47) increases only about linearly with K, so the choice $K = 9$ in this example appears more "efficient" than the choice $K = 4$.

Recall from Section 10.2 that for this same example we would need a p about as large as 10^9 for our first-order method to yield an interval solution of width $w(Y(p)(.05)) \leq 10^{-9}$; whereas, for the ninth-order method above, $K = 9$, we can achieve $w(Y(.05)) \leq 10^{-9}$ (in fact, $\leq 10^{-11}$) with *one* evaluation of (10–47), which requires twenty or so interval arithmetic operations.

As another example, consider the initial-value problem, for $y(x) = (y_1(x), y_2(x))$,

$$\frac{dy_1(x)}{dx} = y_2(x) = f_1(y(x))$$
$$\frac{dy_2(x)}{dx} = -y_1(x) = f_2(y(x)) \qquad (10\text{–}50)$$

with $y_1(0) = 0$, $y_2(0) = 1$.

For this example, we have

$$f_1^{(0)} = y_2, \qquad f_1^{(1)} = y_1, \ldots$$
$$f_2^{(0)} = -y_1, \qquad f_2^{(1)} = -y_2, \ldots$$

or, using the matrix notation,

$$C = \begin{pmatrix} 0 & 1 \\ -1 & 0 \end{pmatrix}$$

we have for $f(y) = \begin{pmatrix} f_1(y) \\ f_2(y) \end{pmatrix} = Cy$, and $y_0 = \begin{pmatrix} 0 \\ 1 \end{pmatrix}$,

$$f^{(0)}(y) = Cy$$
$$f^{(1)}(y) = C^2 y$$
$$\vdots$$
$$f^{(J)}(y) = C^{j+1} y \tag{10-51}$$

We will put

$$F^{(J)}(Y) = C^{j+1} Y \tag{10-52}$$

for the interval extensions of the $f^{(J)}(y)$. Notice that

$$C^2 = -I = -\begin{pmatrix} +1 & 0 \\ 0 & +1 \end{pmatrix}$$

From (10–52), we have

$$\frac{F^{(K)}(y_0)}{K!} = \frac{C^{K+1} y_0}{K!}$$

and

$$\left| \frac{F^{(K)}(y_0)}{K!} \right| = \frac{|y_0|}{K!} = \frac{1}{K!}$$

From (10–38) we have, for this example,

$$h = \begin{cases} (\epsilon K!)^{1/K} & \text{if} \quad (K!\epsilon)^{1/(K+1)} \geq 1 \\ (\epsilon K!)^{1/(K+1)} & \text{if} \quad (K!\epsilon)^{1/(K+1)} < 1 \end{cases}$$

For simplicity, we will estimate the factorial by Stirling's formula in order to more easily see the kind of h's the procedure gives for various values of K. Thus $K!$ is approximately (asymptotic to) $\sqrt{2\pi K}(K/e)^K$. Based on this estimate and the above recipe we will choose h, for this example, to be

$$h = \frac{K}{2} e^{1/K} \tag{10-53}$$

Using this h, we find $A^{(0)}$ from (10–39)

$$A^{(0)} = y_0 + Cy_0[0, h] = \begin{pmatrix} [0, h] \\ 1 \end{pmatrix}$$

For this example, (10–32) becomes

$$Y(x) = \left\{ I + \sum_{j=1}^{K-1} \frac{C^j}{j!} x^j \right\} y_0 + \frac{C^K}{K!} A^{(0)} x^K \tag{10-54}$$

and it turns out that [using (10–54), (10–53)] $Y([0, h]) \not\subset A^{(0)}$. So we put

$$A^{(1)} = \left\{ I + \sum_{j=1}^{K-1} \frac{C^j}{j!}[0, h]^j \right\} y_0 + \frac{C^K}{K!} A^{(0)}[0, h]^K$$

and compute a new $Y([0, h])$ using (10–40), which turns out to be (using the interval form indicated here)

$$Y([0, h]) = \left\{ I + \sum_{j=1}^{K-1} \frac{C^j}{j!}[0, h]^j \right\} y_0 + \frac{C^K}{K!} A^{(1)}[0, h]^K$$

Clearly, this will *not* be contained in $A^{(1)}$. Continuing through the steps of our procedure, we find from step (3) that

$$Y\left(\left[0, \frac{h}{2}\right]\right) = \left\{ I + \sum_{j=1}^{K-1} \frac{C^j}{j!}\left[0, \frac{h}{2}\right]^j \right\} Y_0 + \frac{C^K}{K!} A^{(1)}\left[0, \frac{h}{2}\right]^K \qquad (10\text{–}55)$$

is contained in $A^{(1)}$, provided ϵ in (10–53) is small enough.

PROBLEM 10.5. For the example (10–50) just discussed, put $K = 10$ and $\epsilon = 10^{-10}$; using h given by (10–53) show that $Y([0, h/2])$ given by (10–55) is contained in $A^{(1)}$. Find a bound on $\max_{x \in [0, h/2]} w(Y(x))$ for $Y(x)$ given by (10–40) in this example.

We will return to the discussion of the Kth-order method after the next chapter, which deals with the machine generation of Taylor coefficients. In particular we will consider, in a later section, the problem of an efficient choice of K, the number of terms in the Taylor series with interval remainders.

REFERENCES

1. BIRKHOFF, G.D., "Dynamical systems," *Colloq. Pub. A.M.S.*, 9 (1927).
2. HENRICI, P., *Discrete Variable Methods in Ordinary Differential Equations*. New York: John Wiley & Sons, Inc., 1962.
3. HENRICI, P., "The propagation of error in the digital integration of ordinary differential equations," in L.B. Rall, ed., *Error in Digital Computation*, vol. 1, pp. 185–205. New York: John Wiley & Sons, Inc., 1965.
4. INCE, E.L., *Ordinary Differential Equations*. New York: Dover Publications, Inc., 1953.
5. MOORE, R.E., "The automatic analysis and control of error in digital computation based on the use of interval numbers," in L.B. Rall, ed., *Error In Digital Computation*, vol. I, pp. 61–130. New York: John Wiley & Sons, Inc., 1965.

For further references, see L.B. Rall's bibliography in *Error in Digital Computation,* cited above.

11 THE MACHINE GENERATION OF TAYLOR COEFFICIENTS

11.1 INTRODUCTION

In earlier chapters (Sections 8.2 and 10.3) we have discussed interval methods based on Taylor series expansions. In this chapter we will describe a simple procedure which can be programmed so that the computer can, in effect, derive recursion formulas for the coefficients in a Taylor series expansion of a given function. Actually, a computer program such as we have in mind will generate, not formulas, but *subroutines* whose subsequent execution will yield either real or interval values of Taylor coefficients up to some desired order, evaluated at a given set of real or interval arguments.

The method is applicable to a large class of functions including rational functions, and functions expressible by *composition* of rational and "elementary" functions such as exp, log, sin, cos, arctan, and any function which satisfies a rational differential equation.

The method can also be used to generate the *Jacobian* matrix of partial derivatives of a system of functions. We include a description of this application as well, since in a later chapter we will present an interval method for systems of ordinary differential equations which uses the Jacobian matrix.

The method given in the next section has been described previously by Moore [1] and has been programmed for the IBM 7094 computer by H. R. Jaschke as part of a SHARE program [3] using our Kth-order interval method for solving the initial-value problem in ordinary differential equations.

It has also been programmed by A. Reiter at the Mathematics Research

Center, University of Wisconsin, for the CDC 1604 computer as a separate "package" for use on functions written in FORTRAN-type statements and also, as part of a CDC 1604 interval-differential-equations-solving routine similar to the one mentioned above for the IBM 7094.

In a later chapter we will quote some numerical results obtained with these programs.

11.2 RATIONAL DIFFERENTIAL EQUATIONS

Actually the method we will present is applicable essentially to the Taylor expansion of functions satisfying *rational* differential equations. In this section we will show that this is a rather larger class of functions than it may appear at first glance.

By the *composition* of two real-valued functions f and g we mean the real-valued function whose values are given by $f(g(x))$. The "chain rule" for the derivative of the *composite* function gives us

$$\frac{df(g(x))}{dx} = f'(g(x))g'(x) \tag{11-1}$$

where $f'(g(x))$ means the derivative of f with respect to its argument $g(x)$. If f and g satisfy rational differential equations, then so does their composition. By this, we mean that if $u_1(t)$ satisfies (is a component of a solution of the system)

$$\frac{du_j(t)}{dt} = U_j(u_1(t), \ldots, u_m(t)), \qquad j = 1, 2, \ldots, m \tag{11-2}$$

and $v_1(x)$ satisfies

$$\frac{dv_i(x)}{dx} = V_i(v_1(x), \ldots, v_n(x)), \qquad i = 1, 2, \ldots, n \tag{11-3}$$

then the composite function $w_1(x) = u_1(v_1(x))$ satisfies (is a component of the solution of the system)

$$\frac{dw_j(x)}{dx} = U_j(w_1(x), \ldots, w_m(x))V_1(v_1(x), \ldots, v_n(x))$$

$$j = 1, 2, \ldots, m$$

$$\frac{dv_i(x)}{dx} = V_i(v_1(x), \ldots, v_n(x)) \tag{11-4}$$

$$i = 1, 2, \ldots, n$$

As a consequence of this result (which follows immediately from the chain rule) and the fact that a large number of commonly used functions such as the "elementary" functions satisfy rational differential systems, we can replace a great many differential systems which involve nonrational functions by larger systems which only involve rational functions.

To illustrate with an example, consider the system

$$\frac{dy_1}{dx} = e^{x^2 + y_1^2 \cos y_2}$$

$$\frac{dy_2}{dx} = y_1 \log_e y_2 \tag{11-5}$$

We introduce the new variables [corresponding to the various nonrational and composite functions in (11-5)]

$$y_3(x) = \cos y_2(x)$$
$$y_4(x) = \log_e y_2(x)$$
$$y_5(x) = e^{x^2 + y_1^2 y_3}$$

and also, to make the final system autonomous, we put $y_6(x) = x$ and, furthermore, since the function cos satisfies the *system*

$$\frac{d \cos (t)}{dt} = -\sin (t)$$

$$\frac{d \sin (t)}{dt} = \cos (t)$$

we also introduce the variable

$$y_7(x) = \sin y_2(x)$$

For these variables we have the *rational* system (making use of the chain rule for $dy_3/dx = -y_7 y_2'$, etc.),

$$\frac{dy_1}{dx} = y_5$$

$$\frac{dy_2}{dx} = y_1 y_4$$

$$\frac{dy_3}{dx} = -y_7 y_1 y_4$$

$$\frac{dy_4}{dx} = \left(\frac{1}{y_2}\right) y_1 y_4$$

$$\frac{dy_5}{dx} = y_5(2y_6 + y_1^2(-y_7 y_1 y_4) + 2y_1 y_3 y_5)$$

$$\frac{dy_6}{dx} = 1$$

$$\frac{dy_7}{dx} = y_3 y_1 y_4$$

In the next section we will consider another, more direct, method for the generation of Taylor coefficients of nonrational functions which will enable the computer program for generating the Taylor coefficient subroutines to accept directly functions such as those appearing in (11–5).

For a function y_1 satisfying a rational differential system we generate the Taylor coefficients as follows. Suppose

$$\frac{dy_i}{dx} = f_i(y_1, y_2, \ldots, y_n), \qquad i = 1, 2, \ldots, n$$

where the f_i are rational functions. Display each f_i as the result of the final operation in a finite sequence of arithmetic operations, each of which defines a partial result

$$P_s(x) * Q_s(x) = T_s(x) \tag{11–6}$$

where for each $s = 1, 2, \ldots, S_i$, $*$ is one of the arithmetic operations $+$, $-$, $\cdot$, $/$. Our method consists of applying the appropriate rule for the jth derivative of a sum, difference, product, or quotient corresponding to each partial result $T_s(x)$ so that we obtain a sequence of subroutines for each $d^j T_s(x)/dx^j$ and hence for each $f_i^{(j)}$. Then we put $d^{j+1} y_i/dx^{j+1} = f_i^{(j)}$. Actually, it is more convenient to carry along the factorials and generate the programming for $(1/j!) \, d^j T_s(x)/dx^j$ directly.

For the jth Taylor coefficient $(1/j!) \, d^j P_s(x)/dx^j$ of a function $P_s(x)$ we will use the abbreviation $(P_s(x))_j$. The rules for computing Taylor coefficients of sums, differences, products, and quotients are as follows: for $j \geq 1$

$$(P(x) + Q(x))_j = (P(x))_j + (Q(x))_j \tag{11–7}$$

$$(P(x) - Q(x))_j = (P(x))_j - (Q(x))_j \tag{11–8}$$

$$(P(x)Q(x))_j = \sum_{r=0}^{j} (P(x))_r (Q(x))_{j-r} \tag{11–9}$$

$$\left(\frac{P(x)}{Q(x)}\right)_j = \frac{1}{Q(x)}\left\{(P(x))_j - \sum_{r=1}^{j} (Q(x))_r (T(x))_{j-r}\right\} \tag{11–10}$$

where $T(x) = P(x)/Q(x)$.

PROBLEM 11.1. Verify the recursion formulas (11–9) and (11–10).

Each of the quantities $P_s(x)$, $Q_s(x)$ in (11–6) can be: (1) constant, (2) one of the variables $y_i(x)$, or (3) one of the quantities $T_{s_1}(x)$ for some $s_1 < s$. In displaying the f_i's in a sequence of operations (11–6) we also identify which of the $P_s(x)$ and $Q_s(x)$ are constants so that we can use the simpler forms of (11–7), (11–8), (11–9), (11–10) in case one or both of $P_s(x)$, $Q_s(x)$ are constant. For example, for $Q_s(x) \equiv$ constant $= Q_s$, we have $(Q_s)_j = 0, j \geq 1$ and therefore

$$(P_s(x) \pm Q_s)_j = (P_s(x))_j$$

$$(P_s(x)Q_s)_j = (P_s(x))_j Q_s$$

$$\left(\frac{P_s(x)}{Q_s}\right)_j = \frac{(P_s(x))_j}{Q_s}$$

In order to write the computer program which will generate subroutines for $(y_i(x))_j$ given a differential system

$$(y_i(x))_1 = f_i(y_1, \ldots, y_n), \; i = 1, 2, \ldots, n$$

with rational functions f_i, we set up storage for the quantities $(y_i(x))_j$, $i = 1, 2, \ldots, n; j = 0, 1, 2, \ldots, J$ and also for the quantities $(T_s(x))_j$, $s = 1, 2, \ldots, S_1 + S_2 + \cdots + S_n; j = 1, 2, \ldots, J$ described above with n, J, and $S_1 + S_2 + \cdots + S_n$ restricted to be less than certain numbers chosen on the basis of the amount of storage available on the computer to be used. (For the SHARE program referred to in Section 11.1, we have required that $n \leq 20, J \leq 9, S_1 + S_2 + \cdots + S_n \leq 200$.)

In order to generate subroutines for interval values of $(y_i(x))_j$ to be used, for example, in connection with our Kth-order method for interval solutions of the initial-value problem (Section 10.3), we allocate storage for interval values of the quantities $(y_i(x))_j$ and $(T_s(x))_j$ and generate subroutines which call for rounded-interval arithmetic in the execution of the operations

$$P_s(x) * Q_s(x) = T_s(x)$$

and in the execution of the corresponding computation of $(P_s(x) * Q_s(x))_j$, using the appropriate one of the formulas (11-7), (11-8), (11-9), or (11-10).

We write our program to produce, from the description of the rational functions f_i given to the computer, the sequence of arithmetic operations $P_s(x) * Q_s(x) = T_s(x)$ and the corresponding sequence of subroutines for $(P_s(x) * Q_s(x))_j = (T_s(x))_j$. For $s = S_i$, we have

$$T_{s_i}(x) = f_i(y_1(x), \ldots, y_n(x)) \quad \text{and} \quad (T_{s_i}(x))_j = (f_i(y_1(x), \ldots, y_n(x)))_j$$

We add the machine instructions for

$$(y_i(x))_{j+1} = \left(\frac{1}{j+1}\right)(T_{s_i}(x))_j, \qquad i = 1, 2, \ldots, n$$

The generated subroutine is put together in such a way that given values for $K, y_1, y_2, \ldots, y_n$, it will compute and store upon execution, successively for $j = 1, 2, \ldots, K$, the quantities

$$(T_1)_{j-1}, (T_2)_{j-1}, \ldots, (T_{s_1})_{j-1}, (y_1)_j$$
$$(T_{s_1+1})_{j-1}, (T_{s_1+2})_{j-1}, \ldots, (T_{s_1+s_2})_{j-1}, (y_2)_j \qquad (11\text{-}11)$$
$$\vdots$$
$$(T_{s_1+s_2+\cdots+s_{n-1}+1})_{j-1}, \ldots, (y_n)_j$$

For each multiplication, $P_s(x)Q_s(x) = T_s(x)$, in the computation of the *first* derivatives, i.e., in the evaluation of the functions f_i, the formula (11-9) requires $j + 1$ multiplications and j additions to get $(T_s(x))_j$. For each division, $(P_s(x)/Q_s(x)) = T_s(x)$, the formula (11-10) requires *one* division, j multiplications, and j additions (counting a subtraction as an "addition"). For each addition or subtraction needed to evaluate the set of functions f_i occurring in a given differential system, the formulas (11–7) and (11–8) require, similarly, one addition or subtraction. Therefore, the total number of arithmetic operations required to compute the entire set of quantities

$$\{(T_s)_{j-1}, (y_i)_j | s = 1, 2, \ldots, S_1 + \cdots + S_n; \quad i = 1, 2, \ldots, n;$$
$$j = 1, 2, \ldots, K\}$$

is

$$\left\{KN_1 + \frac{(K-1)K}{2}(N_2 + N_3)\right\} \quad \text{additions or subtractions}$$

$$\left\{\frac{K(K+1)}{2}N_2 + \frac{(K-1)K}{2}N_3\right\} \quad \text{multiplications}$$

$$\{KN_3\} \quad \text{divisions}$$

where N_1 is the number of operations $P_s(x) * Q_s(x) = T_s(x)$ in the evaluation of the functions f_i which are additions or subtractions; N_2 is the number of multiplications in the f_i's; and N_3 is the number of divisions in the f_i's.

Therefore, if $N_0 = N_1 + N_2 + N_3$ is the total number of arithmetic operations in one evaluation of the functions f_i for a given differential system $dy_i/dx = f_i(y_1, y_2, \ldots, y_n)$, then our machine-generated subroutine for evaluating the Taylor coefficients $(y_i)_j$, $i = 1, 2, \ldots, n$, $j = 1, 2, \ldots, K$ at a given initial point $(y_1, y_2, \ldots, y_n)$ will require for its execution a total number of arithmetic operations somewhere between KN_0 and $K(K+1)/2$ N_0, depending on what fraction of the operations in the f_i's are additions, multiplications, or divisions.

In the next section we will discuss a more elaborate set of formulas than the four given by (11–7), (11–8), (11–9), and (11–10) which can be used for a more efficient program for generating Taylor coefficients than the very straightforward one presented in this section.

It should be noted that the subroutine generated by the method of this section (as well as that of the next section) will depend only on the *functions* f_i occurring in a differential system and can be, thereafter, used to find the Taylor coefficients for solutions of that system at any "initial" point, and therefore can be used for our Kth-order interval methods which involve successive Taylor expansions of a given system about each of a sequence of "initial" points $y_0, Y(h^{(1)}), Y(h^{(1)} + h^{(2)}), \ldots$.

Our concern with the number of operations required to get the Taylor coefficients has to do, of course, with the problem of an efficient choice of K, the number of terms in the Taylor series with remainder (see Section 8.2, also Chapter 12).

To use the method of this section to generate Taylor coefficients of a given rational function f of a single real variable x, we can put $x = y_1$ and form the system

$$\frac{dy_1}{dx} = 1, \qquad \frac{dy_2}{dx} = f(y_1) \qquad\qquad (11\text{-}12)$$

Using the method of this section on the system (11-12), we obtain $(y_1)_j = 0$, $j \geq 1$ and

$$(y_2)_{j+1} = \left(\frac{1}{j+1}\right)(f(y_1))_j$$

and, in particular,

$$(f(y_1))_j = \frac{1}{j!}\frac{d^j f(x)}{dx^j} = (T_S(x))_j$$

where the last arithmetic operation in the evolution of f is

$$P_S(x) * Q_S(x) = T_S(x) = f(x)$$

A. Reiter (see Section 11.1) has also programmed the generation of first-order partial derivatives of functions of several variables and of Jacobian matrices of partial derivatives of systems of functions of several variables. His method consists essentially of the following:

Given a function with values $f(y_1, y_2, \ldots, y_n)$, in order to generate $\partial f(y_1, y_2, \ldots, y_n)/\partial y_j$ for some $j = 1, 2, \ldots, n$, we form the differential system

$$\frac{dy_i}{dx} = \delta_{ij} \qquad (\delta_{ij} = 1 \quad \text{if} \quad i = j; \delta_{ij} = 0 \quad \text{if} \quad i \neq j) \qquad (11\text{-}13)$$

$i = 1, 2, \ldots, n$. Then, displaying f as the end result, again, of a finite sequence of operations and regarding the variables y_i as functions of x satisfying (11-13), we obtain

$$\frac{\partial f(y_1, y_2, \ldots, y_n)}{\partial y_j} = (f(y_1(x), y_2(x), \ldots, y_n(x))_1$$

The elements of the Jacobian of a system of functions $f_i(y_1, y_2, \ldots, y_n)$, $i = 1, 2, \ldots, m$, namely $\partial f_i/\partial y_j$, also can be obtained in this way.

11.3 EXTENSION OF THE METHOD TO NONRATIONAL FUNCTIONS

In the previous section we showed how a nonrational system of differential equations such as, for example, (11-5) can be replaced by a larger rational system. In this way the Taylor coefficients of the solutions of such a system can be generated using the method of the previous section based on the formulas for jth derivatives of sums, differences, products, and quotients of pairs of functions, (11-7)–(11-10).

Besides increasing the order of the system, increasing the storage requirements, and increasing the number of operations required to obtain the Taylor coefficients, this approach has the additional disadvantage of producing values of the nonrational functions through solution of the adjoined differential equations, which may increase the difficulty of maintaining interval solutions of narrow width.

Recall that in Section 10.3 (on our Kth-order interval method for interval solutions of the initial-value problem) we did not require that the differential system be rational, but only that certain much more general conditions be satisfied, namely, that we have interval extensions F_i of the functions f_i occurring in the differential system to be solved and interval extensions $F_i^{(j)}$ of $f_i^{(j)}$ satisfying (10–30) and (10–31).

In Section 6.5 we indicated the means of writing interval versions of elementary function subroutines for exp, log, sin, cos, and so on in such a way that for an interval argument X, the resulting interval value $F(X)$ would be very close to and would contain the range of values of the corresponding real function $f(x)$.

In order to handle differential systems with compositions of such functions more directly in the generation of Taylor coefficients of their solutions we can adjoin to the four basic formulas (11–7)–(11–10) for jth derivatives of sums, products, differences, and quotients a set of formulas for the jth derivatives of exp, log, sin, cos, and so on of a given function $P(x)$ giving the jth derivative recursively as a rational function of derivatives of lower order and derivatives of the given function $P(x)$. We will give some such formulas now, derived from the chain rule for derivatives of composite functions and formulas for derivatives of elementary functions from the calculus and the formulas (11–7)–(11–10).

Constant powers: For a real constant a, we have

$$(P^a(x))_j = \frac{1}{P(x)} \sum_{i=0}^{j-1} \left(a - \frac{i(a+1)}{j} \right)(P(x))_{j-1}(P^n(x))_i \quad (11\text{–}14)$$

Exponential:

$$(\exp P(x))_j = \sum_{i=0}^{j-1} \left(1 - \frac{i}{j} \right)(\exp P(x))_i (P(x))_{j-i} \quad (11\text{–}15)$$

Logarithm:

$$(\log_e P(x))_j = \frac{1}{P(x)} \left\{ (P(x))_j - \sum_{i=1}^{j-1} \left(1 - \frac{i}{j} \right)(P(x))_i (\log_e P(x))_{j-i} \right\} \quad (11\text{–}16)$$

for $j > 1$, and $(\log_e P(x))_1 = (P(x))_1 / P(x)$.

Sin and cos:

$$(\sin P(x))_j = \sum_{i=0}^{j-1} \left(\frac{i+1}{j} \right)(\cos P(x))_{j-1-i}(P(x))_{i+1} \quad (11\text{–}17)$$

$$(\cos P(x))_j = -\sum_{i=0}^{j-1} \left(\frac{i+1}{j} \right)(\sin P(x))_{j-1-i}(P(x))_{i+1} \quad (11\text{–}18)$$

To derive (11–17), for example, we write

$$(\sin P(x))_1 = (\cos P(x))(P(x))_1 \qquad (11\text{–}19)$$

and, applying (11–9) to (11–19), we obtain

$$((\sin P(x))_1)_{j-1} = \sum_{i=0}^{j-1} (\cos P(x))_i ((P(x))_1)_{j-1-i}$$

but for any function Q, we have $((Q(x))_1)_{j-r} = (j - r + 1)(Q(x))_{j-r+1}$, so

$$j(\sin P(x))_j = \sum_{i=0}^{j-1} (j - i)(\cos P(x))_i (P(x))_{j-i}$$

which is equivalent (at least, in *real* arithmetic!) to (11–17).

PROBLEM 11.2. Derive a recursion formula for (arc tan $P(x))_j$.

Once we have subroutines for the elementary functions (and for their interval extensions!) and recursion formulas of the kind just discussed, e.g., (11–14), we can generate a subroutine for the Taylor coefficients of solutions of a system such as (11–5), for example, without first going to a larger rational system for (11–5). We need only display the functions occurring in the differential system as the end result of a sequence of arithmetic operations *and* compositions of functions of the type included among those for which we have subroutines and recursion formulas.

For the example (11–5) we can put

$$y_3(x) = x$$

and add the equation $dy_3(x)/dx = 1$ (to make the system autonomous), and the function

$$f_1(y_1, y_2, y_3) = \exp(y_3^2 + y_1^2 \cos y_2)$$

can be displayed as required by putting

$$y_1^2(x) = T_1(x)$$
$$\cos y_2(x) = T_2(x)$$
$$T_1(x) T_2(x) = T_3(x)$$
$$y_3^2(x) = T_4(x)$$
$$T_4(x) + T_3(x) = T_5(x)$$

and, finally,

$$f_1(y_1, y_2, y_3) = \exp T_5(x)$$

The function $f_2(y_1, y_2, y_3) = y_1 \log_e y_2$ can be appropriately displayed in two steps as

$$\log_e y_2(x) = T_6(x)$$
$$f_3(y_1, y_2, y_3) = y_1(x) T_6(x)$$

Using the corresponding recursion formulas for $(T_s(x))_j$, $s = 1, 2, 3, 4, 5, 6$, the *computer* can put together a subroutine for the Taylor coefficients $(y_1(x))_j$, $(y_2(x))_j$, $(y_3(x))_j$. Given an integer K and real (or interval) values for y_1, y_2, y_3, the subroutine so assembled for this example should compute successively and store, for $j = 1, 2, \ldots, K$, the set of quantities $\{(T_1)_{j-1}, (T_2)_{j-1}, \ldots, (y_3)_j\}$, where

$$(T_1)_{j-1} = \sum_{i=0}^{j-1} (y_1)_i (y_1)_{j-1-i}$$

$$(T_2)_{j-1} = \begin{cases} \cos y_2 & \text{for } j = 1 \\ -\sum_{i=0}^{j-2} \left(\frac{i+1}{j-1}\right)(\sin y_2)_{j-2-i}(y_2)_{i+1} & \text{for } j \geq 2 \end{cases}$$

where $(\sin y_2)_0 = \sin y_2$ and

$$(\sin y_2)_q = \sum_{i=0}^{q-1} \left(\frac{i+1}{q}\right)(T_2)_{q-1-i}(y_2)_{i+1}$$

for $q = 1, 2, \ldots, j - 2$

$$(T_3)_{j-1} = \sum_{i=0}^{j-1} (T_1)_i (T_2)_{j-1-i}$$

$$(T_4)_{j-1} = \sum_{i=0}^{j-1} (y_3)_i (y_3)_{j-1-i}$$

$$(T_5)_{j-1} = (T_4)_{j-1} + (T_5)_{j-1}$$

$$(T_6)_{j-1} = \begin{cases} \log_e y_2 & \text{for } j = 1 \\ \dfrac{(y_2)_1}{y_2} & \text{for } j = 2 \\ \dfrac{1}{y_2}\left\{(y_2)_{j-1} - \sum_{j=1}^{j-2}\left(1 - \dfrac{i}{j-1}\right)(y_2)_i(T_6)_{j-1-i}\right\} & \text{for } j \geq 3 \end{cases}$$

and

$$(f_1)_{j-1} = \begin{cases} \exp T_5 & \text{for } j = 1 \\ \sum_{i=0}^{j-2}\left(1 - \dfrac{i}{j-1}\right)(f_1)_i(T_5)_{j-1-i} & \text{for } j \geq 2 \end{cases}$$

$$(f_2)_{i-1} = \sum_{i=0}^{j-1} (y_1)_i (T_6)_{j-1-i}$$

$$(f_3)_{j-1} = \begin{cases} 1 & \text{if } j = 1 \\ 0 & \text{if } j \geq 2 \end{cases}$$

and, finally,

$$(y_1)_j = \left(\frac{1}{j}\right)(f_1)_{j-1}, \quad (y_2)_j = \frac{1}{j}(f_2)_{j-1}, \quad (y_3)_j = \frac{1}{j}(f_3)_{j-1}$$

For each "elementary" function—a power, exponential, logarithm, sine, cosine, or other function for which we have a programmed interval extension and a programmed recursion formula for jth derivatives—which occurs in the expressions for the functions f_i in a given differential system, the subroutine generated for the jth Taylor coefficients, $j = 1, 2, \ldots, K$ of the components of a solution $y_i(x)$, $i = 1, 2, \ldots, n$, will according to the formulas (11–14), (11–15), (11–16), (11–17), (11–18), . . . require approximately $K(K + 1)/2$ additions and $K(K + 1)/2$ multiplications.

Since the evaluation of the interval extension subroutine for such a function (e.g., exponential) will require certainly at least one multiplication and one addition, we will, with this more direct scheme, still have the resulting fact, as in the previous section, that our machine-generated subroutine for evaluting the Taylor coefficients $(y_i)_j$, $j = 1, 2, \ldots, K$, $i = 1, 2, \ldots, n$, at a given point will require for its execution a total number of arithmetic operations less than $K(K + 1)/2$ times the number required to obtain one evaluation of the set of f_i's, $i = 1, 2, \ldots, n$.

The SHARE program referred to in Section 11.1 uses the approach described in Section 11.2 of an a priori reduction by the user, to a rational system, except square roots are also allowed. On the other hand, the program of A. Reiter referred to in Section 11.1 uses the approach described in this section and allows the user to present differential equations in FORTRAN-type statements including the direct use of powers, logarithms, exponentials, sines, cosines, and arctangents. As we have already mentioned at the end of Section 11.2, Reiter's program also provides for the generation of partial derivatives of first order and hence can generate a subroutine for the Jacobian matrix of the system of functions $f_i(y_1, y_2, \ldots, y_n)$, $i = 1, 2, \ldots, n$. We will use this capability in a later chapter.

In the SHARE program, a slightly different set of recursion formulas is used according to the definition

$$(Q)_j = \frac{1}{j!} \frac{d^j Q}{dx^j} \Delta^j$$

of the *normalized* Taylor coefficients [1]. Actually, the formulas remain unchanged except for $(y_i)_j = (1/j)(f_i)_{j-1}\Delta$ in place of $(y_i)_j = (1/j)(f_i)_{j-1}$. The purpose of the "normalization factor" Δ is to make possible a rescaling of the variables during a computation in case of "overflow" or "underflow." The range of exponents in floating point is less on the IBM 7094 than it is on the CDC 1604; this "normalization" was not considered necessary for the program on the latter computer.

REFERENCES

1. MOORE, R.E., "The automatic analysis and control of error in digital computation based on the use of interval numbers," in L.B. Rall, ed., *Error in Digital*

Computation, Vol. I, esp. pp. 103–112. New York: John Wiley & Sons, Inc., 1965.

2. REITER, A., "Automatic generation of Taylor coefficients (TAYLOR)," MRC Program #3, COOP Organ. Code-WISC, Mathematics Research Center, University of Wisconsin, Madison, Wisconsin.

3. SHARE. The program referred to in Chapter 11 is designated as "ML MDJS, SDA #3210" and is available for the IBM 7094 computer from SHARE Distribution, IBM, Data Processing Division, 112 East Post Road, White Plains, New York 10601. Attn: Manager, DP Program Information Dept.

12 NUMERICAL RESULTS WITH THE Kth-ORDER METHOD

12.1 THE CHOICE OF K IN THE Kth-ORDER METHODS

In Section 8.2 we discussed a Kth-order interval method for definite integrals based on Taylor expansions of the integrand. In Chapter 11 we described a method for the machine generation of Taylor coefficients with the property that the number of arithmetic operations required to evaluate the first K Taylor coefficients of a function is roughly proportional to K^2. Thus, the analysis in Section 8.2 based on estimating the amount of computation time to get a value of $I_{n,K}$ as $nK^2 T_0$ [see (8–21)] leading to a choice of n and K [(8–25), (8–27), (8–28)] for which the estimate of time is approximately minimized subject to a fixed width of the interval result, $w(I_{n,K}) = \epsilon$, was reasonable.

In Section 10.3 we discussed a Kth-order interval method for the initial-value problem in ordinary differential equations. For a given K, we found a procedure by which the computer can obtain a region A over which to bound the remainder term and a corresponding interval of values $[0, h]$ of the independent variable x for which the exact solution $y(x)$ is sure to remain within A.

For the initial-value problem $y' = y^2, y(0) = 1$, we found an interval solution $Y(x)$, (10–47), such that the exact solution satisfies $y(x) \in Y(x)$ for $x \in [0, h/2]$ where $h = (\epsilon/(K + 1))^{1/(K+1)}$ and $0 < \epsilon < K + 1$. And we had, (10–48),

$$w(Y(x)) = x^K\{(1 + h + \cdots + h^{K-1} + h^K(1 + h)^{K+1})^{K+1} - 1\}$$

For small h this becomes, *approximately*,

$$w(Y(x)) = x^K(K + 1)h \leq \frac{\epsilon}{2^K}, \qquad \text{for } x \in \left[0, \frac{h}{2}\right]$$

Indeed, we found, for $\epsilon = 10^{-9}$ and $K = 9$, we had $w(Y(x)) \leq 10^{-11}$ for $x \in [0, .05]$; and for $\epsilon = 10^{-9}, K = 4$, we had $w(Y(x)) \leq 10^{-10}$ for $x \in [0, .0057\ldots]$. These illustrative results were based, of course, on the assumption of an evaluation of the formula (10–47) in infinite-precision-interval arithmetic.

For the particular example at hand it is not difficult to see that the nested form of (10–47), namely

$$Y(x) = (\cdots(A^{(1)})^{K+1}x + 1)x + \cdots + 1)x + 1 \qquad (12\text{–}1)$$

can be evaluated in *rounded*-interval arithmetic with almost no loss of precision if h is small enough for a given K. For then $x \in [0, h/2]$ is small and $A^{(1)}$ given by (10–45) is approximately $[1, 1 + h]$; so $(A^{(1)})^{K+1}$ is approximately $[1, 1 + (K + 1)h]$ and the rounding apart of endpoints produced by the addition of the 1's in (12–1) will be "shifted off" by the multiplication of the x's to a low-order bit or so relative to x. As a result, the final interval number computed for $Y(x)$ in rounded-interval-arithmetic evaluation of (12–1) will be only a low-order bit or so wider than the corresponding infinite-precision-interval evaluation of (12–1).

Indeed it is typically the case that, beginning with exact initial data, the procedure of Section 10.3 for choosing A and h will result in an interval $Y(x_1)$ on the computer of width approximately a low-order bit relative to $|Y(x_1)|$ for $x_1 \leq h/2$, by choosing ϵ in (10–38) to be 2^{-s}, where s is the number of binary places carried in the rounded-interval arithmetic used. The SHARE program mentioned in Chapter 11 was tried on a dozen or so distinct differential systems of various orders with exact initial data and in each case, at the *first* computed point, the interval solution had width about 2^{-27} relative to the magnitude of the solution component, using 27-binary-place floating-point rounded-interval arithmetic. What varies is the *length* of the first step, i.e., h (or x_1).

From (10–38) we can expect h to increase with K; but so does the computing time increase with K.

Ideally, we would like a procedure which could be put on the computer for choosing K, given a particular initial-value problem, such that the computing time required to reach a given value of the independent variable x by a certain number of continuations [i.e., successive Taylor expansions at $0, h^{(1)}, h^{(1)} + h^{(2)}, \ldots$] would be minimized.

To get a rough solution, at least, to this minimization problem we proceed as follows: For $|F^{(K)}(y_0)/K!|$ in (10–38) we will use the estimate

$$\left| \frac{F^{(K)}(y_0)}{K!} \right|^{1/K} = \rho^{-1}$$

where ρ is the radius of convergence of the Taylor series. Furthermore, we estimate h, as given by (10–38), by

$$h(K) = \rho e^{1/K}$$

Now we argue that *if* we were going to use a fixed K, then it would take $n(K) = x/(\bar{\rho}\epsilon^{1/K})$ steps of average size $h(K) = \bar{\rho}\epsilon^{1/K}$ to reach the value x. From Chapter 11, we estimate the computation time to do this as $T(K) = n(K)K^2 T_0$ for some constant $T_0 > 0$. Thus

$$T(K) = \frac{x}{\bar{\rho}\epsilon^{1/K}} K^2 T_0 \tag{12-2}$$

We wish to minimize $T(K)$ by some choice of a positive integer K. Now $T(K)$ has the form: (constant) times $K^2 e^{-1/K}$ as far as its dependence upon K is concerned; therefore we can just as well put $T(K) = K^2(1/\epsilon)^{1/K}$, the constant being the "unit of time." We treat K as a continuous variable and we find that

$$T'(K) = 0 \qquad \text{at } K = \frac{1}{2} \log\left(\frac{1}{\epsilon}\right) \tag{12-3}$$

If we put $\epsilon = 2^{-s}$, then (12-3) gives

$$K = \frac{1}{2} \log 2^s = (0.346\ldots)s$$

To indulge in a little harmless numerology, put $\epsilon = 10^{-d}$; then $K = (1.15\ldots)d$ and we have arrived at the result that *the choice of K, the number of terms in our Kth-order-interval Taylor expansions, which minimizes computation time under the assumptions we have made is about the same as d, the number of equivalent decimal places carried in the rounded-interval arithmetic used.*

After several unsuccessful attempts to find something else that the "best" K should depend on (besides the number of decimal places carried in the machine) and after a number of case studies on the computer using various values of K and a variety of distinct *nonlinear* differential systems and initial conditions and using both single and double-precision rounded-interval arithmetic which showed that the *actually observed* computation time on the computer in each study *was*, in fact, a minimum near $K = (1.15\ldots)d$, we are prepared to conclude that we should go ahead and put $K = (1.15\ldots)d$ in our computer program for the interval solution of the initial-value problem using the Kth-order method of Section 10.3 with Taylor coefficients generated by the computer as described in Chapter 11.

This is exactly what we did in our SHARE program. We had $s = 27$, or $d = 8.13$, and $(1.15\ldots)d = 9.3,\ldots$, so we put $K = 9$. The program operates with single-precision rounded-interval arithmetic. A "double-precision" version (not included in the SHARE program) was also programmed and tested using $K = 19$.

For interval solutions requiring a large number of successive expansions a variant of the procedure for choosing K may be noticeably more efficient when using multiple-precision arithmetic. Namely, we can begin with double (or higher) precision rounded-interval arithmetic and put $\epsilon = 2^{-2s}$

(or $\epsilon = 2^{-ms}$), where s is single-precision binary word length. We then use the corresponding integer nearest $K = (0.346\ldots)\,(2s)$ [or $K = (0.346\ldots)$ (ms)]. We keep track of the width of the resulting interval solution $w(Y(x))$ at the successive points of expansion; if and when $w(Y(x))$ exceeds 2^{-s} (or $2^{-(m-1)s}$) we drop to the next lower precision (rather than using the same precision throughout), e.g., single-precision arithmetic, in the subsequent computations, changing ϵ at this point to $\epsilon = 2^{-s}$ (or $\epsilon = 2^{-(m-1)s}$) and lowering K to $(0.346\ldots)s$ [or $K = (0.346\ldots)\,(m-1)s$].

12.2 NUMERICAL STUDIES ON THE COMPUTER

We will give, in this section, a summary of some numerical results, including actual computation times, using the Kth-order interval method for solving the initial-value problem on the IBM 7094 computer. The results were obtained using the SHARE program referred to, except that the value of K was forcibly changed (from its fixed value 9) for some of the studies as indicated and a few results are quoted for a double-precision (54 bits) version and for a version on the CDC 1604 computer.

Some of the results have previously been reported [4] and are repeated here for their relevance to this work.

Before presenting the numerical results we will first of all summarize the main features of the program, which is based on the methods described in this book. Similar programs can be written for any stored-program digital computer; although their practical value will depend somewhat on the size and speed of the machine. In the next chapter we will discuss some additional (and more sophisticated) techniques intended to provide a basis for the programming of routines for the computer solution, in interval form, of the initial-value problem in ordinary differential equations. These additional techniques will deal especially with the problem of maintaining narrow-interval solutions over long-range integration of differential systems.

We summarize now the *method of the* SHARE *program:* ML MDJS, SDA #3210 (see [3], Chapter 11).

Solution values are obtained in the form of intervals which are printed as an *approximate value*, the midpoint of the interval, and an *error bound*, half the width of the interval. Thus an answer is printed as a pair Y, ϵ such that if y is the exact solution value (or *an* exact solution value, in case of intervals of initial data), then $|y - Y| \leq \epsilon$.

Solutions are obtained in a step-by-step fashion by means of successive expansions in Taylor series truncated at the ninth (or Kth) term. The remainder term in the Taylor series is bounded by the program over interval vectors (n-dimensional rectangles) which the program constructs about each new solution point. The step size is chosen so that the solution remains within the region constructed for all intermediate values between one solution point and the next. This containment is tested by the program.

Arithmetic operations connected with evaluation of the interval solution are carried out in rounded-interval arithmetic using single-precision (27-bit) floating-point machine arithmetic (properly rounded) for the determination of endpoints.

The required Taylor coefficients are evaluated using subroutines generated *by the program* from a given differential system.

The only *required input* to the program is a description of the differential system to be solved and initial values for the solution sought. Initial values can be given either as exact or as intervals of values, i.e., data of the form $x \pm \epsilon$. Constants or *parameters* appearing in the differential equations are also allowed to be given either as exact or as intervals of possible real values.

For the program we are discussing the differential system must be presented in the form of a system of (not more than twenty) first-order differential equations, giving the derivatives $dy_i/dx, i = 1, 2, \ldots, n \leq 20$, explicitly as functions $f_i(y_1, y_2, \ldots, y_n)$ in the form of a finite sequence of "basic" operations (arithmetic operations and square roots in this program) on the variables $y_1, y_2, \ldots, y_n$ and the constants (if any) which occur in the given expressions for $f_i(y_1, \ldots, y_n)$.

Output from an execution of the SHARE program for a given initial-value problem will normally consist of the following:

(1) The differential equations and initial values given.

(2) A formula [essentially (10-40)] for interpolating for solution values with rigorous error bounds at values of the independent variable x between the values where successive Taylor expansions are carried out.

(3) A set of Taylor coefficients to be used with (2) over the first expansion interval $[0, x_1]$ and at each new expansion point $x_1, x_2, \ldots$.

(4) The value of x_p and the interval solution Y_i, ϵ_i ($i = 1, 2, \ldots, n$, for an nth-order system) at x_p, along with a set of Taylor coefficients $(Y_i)_j$, $i = 1, 2, \ldots, n, j = 1, 2, \ldots, K$ to be used with (2) for $x \in [x_{p-1}, x_p]$. If the exact solution corresponding to a particular set of real values from the initial intervals is $y_i(x_p), i = 1, 2, \ldots, n$, then we will have $|y_i(x_p) - Y_i| \leq \epsilon_i, i = 1, 2, \ldots, n$.

(5) The program is also supposed to print out the actual time required for the computation. The program will continue to produce interval solutions of the form (4) until a singularity is approached causing the computation to stop with an "error message," such as: "THE PROGRAM IS UNABLE TO BOUND DERIVATIVES OVER THE REGION...," *or* until it is taken off the computer.

There are various "options" provided, such as deleting the printing of the Taylor coefficients, stopping the solution at some specified x_F, requiring the *computer* to determine and print out interpolated values with error bounds at specified values of x [which may be given either in the form of a table of values or in the form $x = O(\Delta x)x_F$], requiring the computer to continue the solution for a specified number of expansion points, say $P = 5$, to get interval solutions at some x_1, x_2, x_3, x_4, x_5.

The following are some examples of actual results obtained with the program.

EXAMPLE 1
Input:

$$\frac{dy}{dx} = y^2, \quad y(0) = 1$$

Output (for the 1st, 2nd, 25th, and 87th computed points deleting Taylor coefficient print-out):

SOLUTION AT X(1) = .044199569

Y = 1.0462435   ERROR BOUND = $7.4505806 \cdot 10^{-8}$

SOLUTION AT X(2) = .17553912

Y = 1.2129139   ERROR BOUND = $1.1920929 \cdot 10^{-7}$

SOLUTION AT X(25) = .92183263

Y = 12.793067   ERROR BOUND = $1.5974045 \cdot 10^{-5}$

SOLUTION AT X(87) = .99986639

Y = 7486.0633   ERROR BOUND = 5.6754150

At this point, the program stopped itself with the final message:

PROGRAM UNABLE TO BOUND DERIVATIVES OVER-

X = .99986639

Y = 7486.0641 $\pm$ 5.6762085

TIME REQUIRED FOR COMPUTATION = 0.50 MINUTES.

Even in floating point it is possible to exceed the range of values of possible single-precision machine numbers. The program tests for this, and this is what caused the termination of the above computation.

EXAMPLE 2
Input:

$$\frac{d^2y}{dx^2} = 6y^2 + \lambda x$$

Actually, we had to rewrite this as

$$y_1^2 = T_1$$
$$6T_1 = T_2$$
$$\lambda y_3 = T_3$$
$$T_2 + T_3 = f_2$$
$$\frac{dy_1}{dx} = y_2$$
$$\frac{dy_2}{dx} = f_2$$
$$\frac{dy_3}{dx} = 1$$

For the initial values

$$x = y_3(0) = 0$$
$$y(0) = y_1(0) = 1$$
$$\frac{dy}{dx}(0) = y_2(0) = 0$$

and for *each* of the values $\lambda = 0, 1, 2, 3, 4, 5$, we asked for interval solutions at $x = 0(.01)1.00$ (i.e., at $x = 0, .01, .02, \ldots, 1.00$).

Output: Interval solutions of the form $Y \pm \epsilon$ were obtained as desired. For example, at $x = 1.00$, with $\lambda = 5$, the computer gave

$Y_1 = 31.071414$ ERROR BOUND $= 2.4199486 \cdot 10^{-5}$

$Y_2 = 346.76896$ ERROR BOUND $= 4.0626526 \cdot 10^{-4}$

$Y_3 = 1.0000000$ ERROR BOUND $= 1.6391277 \cdot 10^{-7}$

The largest error bounds among the entire set of values obtained were 2 in the seventh decimal digit for Y_1 (i.e., for y) and 4 in the seventh decimal digit for Y_2 (i.e., for dy/dx). These occurred at $x = 1.00, \lambda = 5$ as given above.

The total computation required 1.5 minutes on the IBM 7094 computer. The above example is taken from [1]. See also [4].

EXAMPLE 3
   Input:

$$\frac{dy}{dx} = xy(y - 2)$$

(after reduction to "basic steps"),

$$y(0) = 1.0$$

Obtain solution at $x = 0(.02)1.00$.

Output: The maximum width of the computed interval solutions occurred at $x = 1.00$ where the program produced

$$Y = .53788284 \pm 1.3 \cdot 10^{-7}$$

or

$$y(1) \in [.53788271, .53788297]$$

The exact solution to this problem is

$$y(x) = \frac{2}{1 + e^{x^2}} \quad \text{and} \quad y(1) = .5378828427\ldots$$

EXAMPLE 4
   Input:

$$\frac{dy}{dx} = \sqrt{1 - y^2}$$

$$x_0 = 1.4, \quad x_F = 1.54, \quad y(1.4) = .98544973 \pm 5 \cdot 10^{-9}$$

Output: After 21 computed points (successive Taylor expansions) the program reached $x = 1.54$, where it found an interval solution of width $3.8 \cdot 10^{-7}$. The time required was .17 minutes.

EXAMPLE 5
   Input:

$$y' = -16xy$$

$$x_0 = -.75$$

$$y(x_0) = 2.2159242 \cdot 10^{-3} \pm 1.5 \cdot 10^{-11}$$

obtain solution at $x = -.75(.25).75$.

Output: The time required to obtain the (single-precision) interval solutions at $x = -.75(.25).75$ was .14 minutes.

A corresponding computation was carried out with a double-precision (54 bits) version of the program using $K = 19$ terms in the Taylor expansions. The double-precision interval solution took .36 minutes and required 20 expansions.

At $x = 0, .25, .50$ the *error bounds* for the single- and double-precision results were as follows:

	$x = 0$	$x = .25$	$x = .50$
s. p.	$1.4 \cdot 10^{-7}$	$2.3 \cdot 10^{-7}$	$10.5 \cdot 10^{-7}$
d. p.	$1 \cdot 10^{-15}$	$2 \cdot 10^{-15}$	$8 \cdot 10^{-15}$

The example is taken from pp. 85–86 of reference [3] to Chapter 10.

EXAMPLE 6
   Input: The differential equations for the so-called "restricted three-body problem" were given as

$$y_1'' - 2y_2' = y_1 - \frac{\mu(y_1 - 1 + \mu)}{r^3} - \frac{(1 - \mu)(y_1 + \mu)}{R^3}$$

$$y_2'' + 2y_1' = y_2 - \frac{\mu y_2}{r^3} - \frac{(1 - \mu)y_2}{R^3}$$

where

$$r = \{(y_1 - 1 + \mu)^2 + y_2^2\}^{1/2}$$
$$R = \{(y_1 + \mu)^2 + y_2^2\}^{1/2}$$

Putting $\mu = .01215$, the equations become a mathematical model for the motion of a vehicle in "free-fall" in the earth-moon gravitational field.

With the initial values $x = 0$, $y_1(0) = 1.2$, $y_2(0) = 0$, $y_1'(0) = 0$, $y_2'(0) = -1.0493575$ given in [2], we made *a study of the computer time required to reach the value* $x = 1.00$ for various values of K, the number of terms used in the Taylor expansions. We list here some results of the study.

In each case, for the various values of K, the program chose the "step size" h from (10–38) in an attempt to keep the "local truncation error" (i.e., the width of our remainder term) of comparable size to a low-order bit in the machine precision used. We used $\epsilon = 2^{-26}$ in (10–38) as a *fixed value* in our single-precision SHARE program.

Output:

K = no. of terms in expansions	Computation time (mins.)	No. of expansions	Max. error bound
5	4.26	171	$1.65 \cdot 10^{-5}$
6	3.48	98	$1.01 \cdot 10^{-5}$
7	3.21	67	$7.30 \cdot 10^{-6}$
8	3.15	51	$6.18 \cdot 10^{-6}$
9	3.38	43	$5.61 \cdot 10^{-6}$

Similar case studies of computation time versus K were made for these and other nonlinear differential equations with various initial values with the result in all examples tried that the computation time to reach a given value of x was minimum near $K = 9$ for our single-precision version of the SHARE program. See Section 12.1.

EXAMPLE 7

For the differential equation $dy/dx = y^2$ (see Example 1), with the initial value $y(0) = 1$, we found that the computation time to reach $x = .75$ was minimum near $K = 19$ for the double-precision version of the program. For each K the error bound at $x = .75$ was about 10^{-14} and the computation times *in minutes* were, for example,

K = no. of terms in expansions	Computation time
10	.35
15	.21
19	.19

For the double-precision version of the program, we set $\epsilon = 2^{-53}$ in (10–38).

EXAMPLE 8

Input:

$$\frac{dy_1}{dx} = y_2, \qquad \frac{dy_2}{dx} = -y_1$$

$$y_1(0) = 0, \qquad y_2(0) = 1.0$$

Find interval solution at $x = 0(.5)9.0$.

Output: Interval solutions were printed at each $x = 0(.5)9.0$ of the form $Y_1 \pm \epsilon_1$, $Y_2 \pm \epsilon_2$. The computation took .05 minutes. In particular, at $x = 3.0, 6.0, 9.0$ the results actually printed were:

SOLUTION AT X = 3.0

Y1 = .14112000   ERROR BOUND = 4.97... $\cdot 10^{-7}$

Y2 = −.98999248   ERROR BOUND = 4.99... $\cdot 10^{-7}$

SOLUTION AT X = 6.0

Y1 = −.27941547   ERROR BOUND = 1.04... $\cdot 10^{-5}$

Y2 = .96017025   ERROR BOUND = 1.04... $\cdot 10^{-5}$

SOLUTION AT X = 9.0

Y1 = .41211843   ERROR BOUND = 2.1... $\cdot 10^{-4}$

Y2 = −.91113021   ERROR BOUND = 2.1... $\cdot 10^{-4}$

The actual errors in the *midpoints* of the interval solutions, i.e., the printed values of Y1, Y2 for $x = 0(.5)9.0$, were in no case greater than $6 \cdot 10^{-8}$ by comparison with published tables of sine and cosine.

We will investigate the growth of error bounds in these examples in the next chapter and we will consider some methods for reducing them.

EXAMPLE 9

For the differential equation

$$\frac{d^2y}{dx^2} + \sin y = 0$$

describing the motion of a pendulum swinging through an angle $y(x)$ at time x, we obtained results using both the SHARE program and also the program of A. Reiter (see Chapter 11) written for the CDC 1604 computer.

The initial values $y(0) = 0$, $y'(0) = .01$ were supplied along with the differential equation, which was written as

$$\frac{dy_1}{dx} = y_2$$

$$\frac{dy_2}{dx} = -y_3$$

$$\frac{dy_3}{dx} = y_4 y_2$$

$$\frac{dy_4}{dx} = -y_3 y_2$$

for the SHARE program (making the substitutions $y = y_1, y' = y_2$, $\sin y = y_3$, $\cos y = y_4$); and the differential equation was written as

$$\frac{dy_1}{dx} = y_2$$

$$\frac{dy_2}{dx} = -\sin y_1$$

for Reiter's program (making the substitutions $y = y_1, y' = y_2$).

The two runs were made on different computers with different word lengths and correspondingly different values of K (see Section 12.1). As expected, the run with the higher machine precision produced narrower interval widths. Somewhat unexpectedly both runs showed the same (multiplicative) factor of increase of interval widths over a given increment in x.

For example, at $x = 9$, corresponding interval widths were $1.8 \cdot 10^{-7}$ and $2.8 \cdot 10^{-6}$, whereas at $x = 12$ they were $3.6 \cdot 10^{-6}$ and $5.6 \cdot 10^{-5}$ for the two programs.

In the next chapter we will discuss a source of growth of interval widths using these programs.

REFERENCES

1. DAVIS, H. T., *Introduction to Nonlinear Differential and Integral Equations* esp. Table I, Appendix 4. New York: Dover Publications, Inc., 1962.
2. FEHLBERG, E., "Runge-Kutta type formulas of high-order accuracy and their application to the numerical integration of the restricted problem of three bodies," *International Symposium on Analogue and Digital Techniques Applied to Aeronautics*, Liège, Belgium, 1963.
3. MOORE, R. E., J. A. DAVISON, H. R. JASCHKE, and S. SHAYER, "DIFEQ integration routine-user's manual," Technical Report LMSC 6-90-64-6, Lockheed Missiles and Space Co., Palo Alto, California. (1964) (Basis for the SHARE program).

4. MOORE, R. E., "The automatic analysis and control of error in digital computation...," in L. B. Rall, ed., *Error in Digital Computation,* Vol. I. New York: John Wiley & Sons, Inc., 1965.

13 COORDINATE TRANSFORMATIONS FOR THE INITIAL-VALUE PROBLEM

13.1 INTRODUCTION

In Chapters 10, 11, and 12 we have presented a procedure enabling the computer to determine intervals containing exact values of solutions to the initial-value problem for systems of ordinary differential equations. In Chapter 12 we also gave examples of numerical results actually obtained using the procedure.

Denote the exact solution of the initial-value problem

$$\frac{dy}{dx} = f(y), \qquad y(0) = y_0$$

by $y(x, y_0)$. Then

$$\frac{\partial y(x, y_0)}{\partial x} = f(y(x, y_0)) \quad \text{and} \quad y(0, y_0) = y_0$$

We suppose y and f are n-dimensional real vectors.

Denote the interval-vector-valued result of our procedure described in Chapters 10, 11, 12 obtained using s binary-digit arithmetic ($s = 27$ for the single-precision SHARE program) by $Y^{(s)}(x, y_0)$.

For a given initial-value problem $Y^{(s)}(x, y_0)$ will be defined for a certain range of values of x, say for $x \in [0, x_F]$. For $x \in [0, x_F]$, we have $y(x, y_0) \in Y^{(s)}(x, y_0)$, that is, the interval solution *contains* the exact solution.

For a fixed $x \in [0, x_F]$ the *width* of $Y^{(s)}(s, y_0)$ [i,e., the maximum width of the components $Y_i^{(s)}(x, y_0)$, $i = 1, 2, \ldots, n$] is of order 2^{-s}, i.e., $w(Y^{(s)}(x, y_0))2^{+s}$ is bounded as s increases indefinitely. By using high enough machine precision in the arithmetic computation of endpoints of intervals

131

the interval-vector solution will become arbitrarily narrow in width. The procedure (see Section 12.1) adjusts step size between successive expansions to keep the remainder terms of order 2^{-s}.

On the other hand, for a fixed s, the width of $Y^{(s)}(x, y_0)$ will *increase* from one expansion point to the next. In fact $w(Y^{(s)}(x, y_0))$ will increase as x increases. This follows from the fact that for any two intervals $[a, b]$, $[c, d]$ we have

$$w([a, b] + [c, d]) = w([a + c, b + d]) = (b + d) - (a + c)$$
$$= (b - a) + (d - c) = w([a, b]) + w([c, d])$$

Since our interval solutions have the form [see (10–40)]

$$Y^{(s)}(x, y_0) = Y^{(s)}(x_p, y_0) + (x - x_p)F$$

(with F consisting of the terms in the Taylor expansion involving the derivatives of f), it follows that, for $x > x_p$,

$$w(Y^{(s)}(x, y_0)) \geq w(Y^{(s)}(x_p, y_0))$$

with equality only in the trivial case $F \equiv 0$.

As we mentioned in Section 10.1, the vector-valued function f defines a "vector field" on the "phase space" of the differential system, and through each point y_0 in the phase space there passes a solution to the differential system which can be regarded as a curve tangent to the vector field at each point on the curve. If we have found an interval vector $Y(x_1, y_0)$ containing $y(x_1, y_0)$ for a certain x_1 and y_0, then through each point $p \in Y(x_1, y_0)$ there passes a solution curve $y(x, p)$ satisfying the differential system for some range of values of x and such that $y(0, p) = p$. The set of points

$$S = \{y(x_2, p)|p \in Y(x_1, y_0)\} \tag{13–1}$$

for some $x_2 > 0$ will contain, in particular, the point $y(x_1 + x_2, y_0)$ since $y(x_1, y_0) \in Y(x_1, y_0)$ and

$$y(x_1 + x_2, y_0) = y(x_2, y(x_1, y_0))$$

Our interval solution at $x = x_1 + x_2$ to the initial-value problem $dy/dx = f(y)$, $y(0) = y_0$, namely $Y(x_1 + x_2, y_0)$, will contain the set S if a new expansion is to be carried out at x_1 because our procedure for continuing the interval solutions consists in putting $Y(x_1, y_0)$ as the new initial value, and for $x > x_1$ our interval solution $Y(x, y_0)$ will contain *all* real solutions $y(x)$ to initial-value problems with $y(x_1) \in Y(x_1, y_0)$ satisfying the given differential system.

On the other hand, the set S, (13–1), will *not* usually be an interval vector. The vector field defined by f will rotate and distort a region of points $\{y(x, y_0)|y_0 \in Y_0\}$ consisting of the set of solutions at x through "initial points" y_0 in an interval vector Y_0 as x increases.

Thus, the nature of our procedure for continuing the interval solution by successive expansions introduces a source of growth of interval widths beyond what the vector field itself does to the set of real solutions through an interval vector Y_0.

To illustrate, consider Example 8 in Section 12.2, which is also discussed in Section 10.3 [see equation (10-50)].

The differential system can be written in vector form as

$$\frac{dy}{dx} = \begin{pmatrix} 0 & 1 \\ -1 & 0 \end{pmatrix} y \tag{13-2}$$

The solution $y(x, y_0)$ to (13-2) through the initial point y_0 can be represented by

$$y(x, y_0) = T(x)y_0 \tag{13-3}$$

where $T(x)$ is the matrix

$$T(x) = \begin{pmatrix} \cos x & \sin x \\ -\sin x & \cos x \end{pmatrix} \tag{13-4}$$

Equation (13-3) says, in effect, that the "flow" in the "phase space" [i.e., the (y_1, y_2) plane] induced by the vector field defined by (13-2) consists of a rigid rotation about the origin of the (y_1, y_2) plane, with uniform angular "velocity."

Figure 13.1 illustrates the effect of this "flow" or motion on an interval vector $Y_0 = (Y_1, Y_2)$.

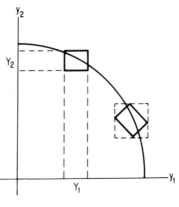

Fig. 13.1

The rotated rectangle consists of the set of solution points $\{y(x, y_0) | y_0 \in Y_0\}$ at some $x > 0$, passing through initial points y_0 in the interval vector Y_0 (the unrotated rectangle) at $x = 0$.

It should be plain that if Y_0 represents our interval solution to (13-2) obtained after one or more expansions starting with some initial value (or interval vector of values) and if we are beginning a new expansion about Y_0 as an initial interval vector (see Section 10.3), then our interval solution $Y(x, Y_0)$ will be an interval vector (an unrotated rectangle) containing the rotated rectangle in Fig. 13.1. This will be a rectangle at least as large as the dotted rectangle in Fig. 13.1 shown containing the rotated rectangle. Subsequent expansions will continue to produce interval vectors, unrotated rectangles, of ever-increasing width. This is actually the principal source of the observed growth of widths of interval solutions seen in Example 8, Section 12.2.

It might seem reasonable to suppose that this source of growth of interval width would be diminished by taking more frequent expansions, i.e., by reducing our "step size" between successive Taylor expansions with interval remainder. But this is not so. In fact, in the example under discussion, (13–2), suppose we were to carry out a new expansion at every increment of h in the independent variable x. By the argument just given, the successive widths of the interval solutions at $h, 2h, 3h, \ldots$ would satisfy

$$w_{n+1} \geq (\sin h + \cos h)w_n \qquad (13\text{–}5)$$

Given any $\theta, 0 < \theta < 1$, for small enough h, (13–5) implies

$$w_{n+1} \geq (1 + \theta h)w_n \qquad (13\text{–}6)$$

From (13–6) we have, for a fixed $Nh = x$,

$$w_N \geq (1 + \theta h)^N w_0 = (1 + \theta h)^{x/h} w_0$$

and

as $\qquad h \to 0, \qquad (1 + \theta h)^{x/h} \to e^{\theta x}$

Since we can choose θ arbitrarily close to 1, this means that as $h \to 0$ the widths of our interval solutions at x obtained with expansions every step of size h approach exponential growth as a function of x. If $x = 2\pi$, this amounts to a factor of increase of $e^{2\pi}$, which is roughly 500, per "revolution" of the solution about the origin. In other words, in this example, (13–2), we can expect to lose more than two decimal places of sharpness (excess width of interval solution beyond actual difference between midpoint of interval solution and exact result) in our error bounds every time x increases by 2π if our step size between successive expansions is small. This agrees with the observed rate of growth of error bounds in Example 8, Section 12.2.

For the particular initial-value problem we have been discussing the solution is represented by (13–3), and therefore the *coordinate transformation*

$$y = T(x)z \qquad (13\text{–}7)$$

gives us a "moving" (z_1, z_2) coordinate frame with respect to which the differential system (13–2) becomes

$$\frac{dz}{dx} = 0 \qquad (13\text{–}8)$$

Since $T(0) = I = \begin{pmatrix} 1 & 0 \\ 0 & 1 \end{pmatrix}$, we have, from (13–8) and (13–7),

$$z(x, z_0) \equiv z_0 = \{T(0)\}^{-1} y_0 = y_0$$

The differential system (13–8) can, of course, be solved *exactly* by our interval method, and therefore the coordinate transformation (13–7) is a very good one to use in connection with the initial-value problem (13–2), $y(0) = y_0$, from the point of view of reducing the growth of widths of interval solutions.

In the next section we will describe a general procedure *which can be programmed for digital computers* for deriving a moving coordinate frame (i.e., an x-dependent coordinate transformation) for a given initial-value problem which will reduce the growth of widths of interval solutions. The procedure can be put together with our Kth-order interval methods and the entire scheme made into a computer program. This has, in fact, been done; numerical results obtained using such a program will be given.

13.2   A TRANSFORMATION BASED ON THE CONNECTION MATRIX

As in the previous section, we denote the n-dimensional real vector solution to the initial-value problem

$$\frac{dy}{dx} = f(y), \quad y(0) = y_0 \quad \text{by} \quad y(x, y_0)$$

We define the *connection matrix* for the solution $y(x, y_0)$ as the matrix $C(x, y_0)$ with elements

$$C_{ij}(x, y_0) = \frac{\partial y_i(x, y_0)}{\partial (y_0)_j}, \qquad i, j = 1, 2, \ldots, n \tag{13-9}$$

Using a slightly more precise notation, we mean by (13.9) that

$$C_{ij}(x, y_0) = \left. \frac{\partial y_i(x, \bar{y})}{\partial \bar{y}_j} \right|_{\bar{y} = y_0}$$

The term "connection" matrix is based on a related concept in differential geometry.

The elements of the connection matrix (13–9) indicate the *sensitivity* of the solution components, $y_i(x, y_0)$, with respect to small changes in the initial values $(y_0)_j, j = 1, 2, \ldots, n$.

If each component $f_i(y)$ of $f(y)$ is analytic in the components y_j of y in an open set about y_0, then for sufficiently small h we can expand the solution $y(x, y_1)$ for y_1 near y_0 in powers of the differences $(y_1)_j - (y_0)_j$, $j = 1, 2, \ldots, n$ about $y(x, y_0)$ for $x \in [0, h]$. In this way we obtain

$$y(x, y_1) = y(x, y_0) + C(x, y_0)(y_1 - y_0) + O(|y_1 - y_0|^2) \tag{13-10}$$

From

$$\frac{\partial}{\partial x} \left(\frac{\partial y_i(x, \bar{y})}{\partial \bar{y}_j} \right) = \frac{\partial}{\partial \bar{y}_j} \left(\frac{\partial y_i(x, \bar{y})}{\partial x} \right)$$

we have

$$\frac{\partial C_{ij}(x, y_0)}{\partial x} = \frac{\partial f_i(y(x, y_0))}{\partial (y_0)_j} \tag{13-11}$$

We denote the *Jacobian matrix* of the vector function f evaluated at $y(x, y_0)$ by $J(x, y_0)$.

The matrix $J(x, y_0)$ has elements

$$J_{ij}(x, y_0) = \frac{\partial f_i(y)}{\partial y_j}\bigg|_{y = y(x, y_0)} \tag{13-12}$$

Using the "chain rule" for partial derivatives, we find that

$$\frac{\partial f_i(y(x, y_0))}{\partial (y_0)_j} = \sum_{m=1}^{n} J_{im}(x, y_0) C_{mj}(x, y_0) \tag{13-13}$$

and therefore [by (13-11) and (13-13)] we have

$$\frac{\partial C(x, y_0)}{\partial x} = J(x, y_0) C(x, y_0) \tag{13-14}$$

For a fixed y_0, equation (13-14) is a system of n^2 first-order linear differential equations for the elements $C_{ij}(x, y_0)$ of $C(x, y_0)$, written in matrix form.

From the Taylor expansion of $y(x, y_1)$ in powers of x, we have

$$y(x, y_1) = y_1 + f(y_1)x + O(x^2) \tag{13-15}$$

We find that $C(0, y_0)$ [by comparison of (13-15) and (13-10)] is the identity matrix, I.

From (13-14) and $C(0, y_0) = I$ we can compute $C(x, y_0)$, at least *approximately* as we will see later in this section. In Section 11.2 we described a means whereby the *computer* can generate a subroutine for the Jacobian matrix $J(x, y_0)$.

We now define our transformation of coordinates based on (13-10) by

$$y(x, y_1) = y(x, y_0) + C(x, y_0)z(x, y_0, y_1) \tag{13-16}$$

or more simply,

$$y = y(x, y_0) + C(x, y_0)z \tag{13-17}$$

Since $C(0, y_0) = I$, it follows that $C(x, y_0)$ will remain nonsingular for some interval of values of x, say for $x \in [0, h]$.

From (13-17) we derive a differential system for $z(x, y_0, y_1)$.
We find from (13-14), (13-17) that

$$\frac{dz}{dx} = C^{-}(xy_0,)\{f(y(x, y_0) + C(x, y_0)z) - \frac{\partial y(x, y_0)}{\partial x}$$

$$- J(x, y_0)C(x, y_0)z\} \tag{13-18}$$

Since $C(x, y_0)$ and $J(x, y_0)$ do not usually commute, we cannot distribute the multiplication by C^{-1} in (13-18) to simplify the last term.

From (13-16) we find, for the initial value of z,

$$y(0, y_1) = y_1 = y_0 + Iz(0, y_0, y_1)$$

or

$$z(0, y_0, y_1) = y_1 - y_0 \qquad (13\text{-}19)$$

The *idea* now is to use the transformation (13-16) and the derived initial-value problem (13-18) and (13-19) to follow, with our interval methods, the *set* of solutions to $dy/dx = f(y)$ corresponding to intervals of initial values.

In particular, if we put $y_1 = y_0$, then $z(0, y_0, y_0) = 0$ and, in fact, from (13-16) we find that $z(x, y_0, y_0) \equiv 0$; therefore, form (13-18), $dz/dx \equiv 0$.

If we consider a *set* of values for y_1, say $y_1 \in y_0 + B$, where B is an interval vector of width ϵ, then $z(0, y_0, y_1) \in B$, $w(B) = \epsilon$. From (13-18) we find, in this case, that

$$\left. \frac{dz}{dx} \right|_{x=0} = \{ f(y_0 + z(0, y_0, y_0)) - f(y_0) - J(0, y_0)z(0, y_0, y_1) \}$$

and therefore $dz/dx|_{x=0} \in A$ for some interval vector A such that $w(A) = O(\epsilon^2)$.

By continuity, the right-hand side of (13-18) will remain small of order ϵ^2 for $x \in [0, h]$ if ϵ is sufficiently small.

Therefore, hopefully, our interval method based on Taylor expansions with interval remainder applied to (13-18) with $z(0, y_0, y_0 + B)$ will produce, at least for small $w(B)$, an interval solution for $x \in [0, h]$ such that

$$Z(x) = B + O((w(B))^2) \qquad (13\text{-}20)$$

That is, in the z coordinates, our interval solutions may tend to be very slowly changing interval vectors. The solution in the original y coordinates can be recovered at desired values of x using (13-16), which in this case implies

$$\{ y(x, y_1) | y_1 \in y_0 + B \} \in y(x, y_0) + C(x, y_0)Z(x)$$

We have been presupposing the availability of $y(x, y_0)$, $J(x, y_0)$, and $C(x, y_0)$ up to this point. Now we will discuss a computationally feasible version of the above technique using approximations to $y(x, y_0)$, $J(x, y_0)$, and $C(x, y_0)$.

In the first place, we will approximate $y(x, y_p)$ by

$$y^*(x, y_p) = y_p + \sum_{j=1}^{K-1} (F)_j x^j \qquad (13\text{-}21)$$

where the coefficients $(F)_j$ are interval extensions of the jth Taylor coefficients in the expansion of the solution of $dy/dx = f(y)$ about y_p (see Chapter 11).

The approximation (13-21) to $y(x, y_p)$ will be used in the following procedure only for x in an interval $[x_p, x_p + h]$, after which a new expansion will be obtained, putting a new value y_{p+1} for y_p in (13-21).

For the integer K in (13–21) we will choose $K = d$ for use with a machine arithmetic equivalent to about d decimal places in the computation of interval endpoints (see Chapter 12).

For the Jacobian matrix $J(x, y_p)$ we will use the approximation $J^*(x, y_p)$, with

$$J^*_{ij}(x, y_p) = \frac{\partial f_i(y)}{\partial y_j}\bigg|_{y = y^*(x, y_p)} \tag{13–22}$$

For the connection matrix $C(x, y_0)$ we will use the approximation $C^*(x, y_0)$ given by

$$C^*(x, y_0) = I + J^*(0, y_0)x \tag{13–23}$$

for $x \in [0, h]$, and for $x \in [x_p, x_p + h]$ we will put

$$C^*(x, y_0) = \{I + J^*(x_p, y_p)(x - x_p)\}C^*(x_p, y_0) \tag{13–24}$$

where y_p in (13–24) denotes the same "initial" value of y used in (13–21) for the expansion of $y^*(x, y_p)$ carried out at x_p.

For a sequence of values $x_0, x_1, x_2, \ldots$ at which new expansions of (13–21) are carried out about "initial" values $y_0, y_1, y_2, \ldots$ the corresponding values of $C^*(x_p, y_0)$ are determined by

$$C^*(x_p, y_0) = \{I + J^*(x_{p-1}, y_{p-1})(x_p - x_{p-1})\}C^*(x_{p-1}, y_0) \tag{13–25}$$

From (13–14), we see that (13–24) and (13–25) amount to approximating the solution $C(x, y_0)$ to (13–14) by a matrix function which is "piecewise linear" in x; that is, we solve (13–14) approximately by the Euler method.

For the matrix $C^*(x, y_0)$, we have

$$\frac{\partial C^*(x, y_0)}{\partial x} = J^*(x_p, y_p)C^*(x_p, y_0) \tag{13–26}$$

for $x_p \leq x < x_{p+1}$.

With $y^*(x, y_0)$ defined by $y^*(x, y_0) = y^*(x - x_p, y_p)$ for $x_p \leq x < x_{p+1}$, putting $y_{p+1} = y^*(x_{p+1} - x_p, y_p)$ in (13–21), and with $C^*(x, y_0)$ defined by (13–24) and (13–25), we now modify the transformation (13–26) to the form

$$y(x, \bar{y}) = y^*(x, y_0) + C^*(x, y_0)z(x, y_0, \bar{y}) \tag{13–27}$$

From (13–27) we derive the differential system for z which now becomes

$$\frac{dz}{dx} = C^{*-1}(x, y_0)\left\{f(y^*(x, y_0) + C^*(x, y_0)z) - \frac{\partial y^*(x, y_0)}{\partial x} - \frac{\partial C^*(x, y_0)}{\partial x}z\right\} \tag{13–28}$$

using (13–26) for $\partial C^*(x, y_0)/\partial x$, and

$$\frac{\partial y^*(x, y_0)}{\partial x} = \sum_{j=1}^{K-1} j(F)_j x^{j-1}$$

for $x_p \leq x < x_{p+1}$ [see (13–21)].

From (13–28), if we write $C^*(x, y_0)dz/dx = H$, we obtain, since $\partial^j C^*(x, y_0)/\partial x^j = 0$ for $j \geq 2$,

$$C^*(x_p, y_0)z_p^{(j)} = H_p^{(j)} - (j-1)\frac{\partial C^*(x_p, y_0)}{\partial x}z_p^{(j-1)} \qquad (13\text{–}29)$$

as a recursion relation for the successive derivatives of z at x_p. From (13–29) we see that we only need to invert the matrix C^* at the points of expansion x_p in order to find the Taylor coefficients for the expansion of z at x_p.

For the determination of the remainder term over a region $([x_p, x_{p+1}], A)$ we must invert the interval matrix

$$C^*([x_p, x_{p+1}], y_0) = \{I + J^*(x_p, y_p)[0, x_{p+1} - x_p]\}C^*(x_p, y_0)$$

We can do this, for example, using Hansen's method (see Chapter 5).

Allen Reiter has written a program at the Mathematics Research Center, University of Wisconsin, for the CDC 1604 computer based on the transformation method described in this section and using the Kth-order interval method described in previous chapters to obtain interval solutions of (13–28). He found that in order to keep dz/dx from (13–28) as small as it is supposed to be it is not sufficient to use a straightforward interval extension of (13–28) from a given rational system $dy/dx = f(y)$. However, using the "mean-value form" of the right-hand side of (13–28) (see Section 6.3), Reiter obtained results for the initial-value problem discussed in Example 8, Section 12.2, which verify the possibility of reducing the growth of widths of interval solutions using the transformation method of this chapter. Whereas the SHARE program lost between two and three decimal places of sharpness in error bounds per revolution (increase of 2π in x) for Example 8 (in Section 12.2), the use of the transformation method written as a general program for the CDC 1604 computer along the lines indicated in this section reduced the growth of interval widths for Example 8 to about one decimal place per revolution.

The actual output using the transformation method of this section to be compared with Example 8, Section 12.2, at $x = 3, 6, 9$ was

SOLUTION AT X = 3.0

Y1 =   .14112000805   ERROR BOUND = 5.6... $\cdot 10^{-10}$

Y2 = −.98999249665   ERROR BOUND = 6.2... $\cdot 10^{-10}$

SOLUTION AT X = 6.0

Y1 = − .27941549819   ERROR BOUND = 2.3... $\cdot 10^{-9}$

Y2 =   .96017028692   ERROR BOUND = 2.4... $\cdot 10^{-9}$

SOLUTION AT X = 9.0

$$Y1 = \quad .41211848524 \qquad \text{ERROR BOUND} = 9.3\ldots \cdot 10^{-9}$$

$$Y2 = -.91113026212 \qquad \text{ERROR BOUND} = 9.4\ldots \cdot 10^{-9}$$

The time required for the computation was 4.8 minutes. Al least part of the reason for the slowness of this computation as compared with the .05 minutes for Example 8, Section 12.2, was the fact that the CDC 1604 interval-arithmetic routines had to *simulate* unrounded floating-point arithmetic, which is not available in the machine "hardware," in order to round end-points properly (see Section 3.2).

The ratio of error bounds at $X = 9.0$ to those at $X = 3.0$ was about 400 in Example 8, Section 12.2; here it is reduced to about 16. An over-all reduction in size of error bounds also results from the higher precision of single-precision arithmetic on the CDC 1604 for which $s = 36$ as compared to $s = 27$ bits on the IBM 7094. We used $K = 12$ for the number of terms in the Taylor expansions in the CDC 1604 program.

REFERENCES

1. MOORE, R.E., "Automatic local coordinate transformations to reduce the growth of error bounds in interval computation of solutions of ordinary differential equations," in L. B. Rall, ed., *Error in Digital Computation*, Vol. II. New York: John Wiley & Sons, Inc., 1965.

APPENDICES

APPENDIX 1   ILLUSTRATION OF THE VARIOUS KINDS OF ARITHMETIC USED

1. *Real arithmetic* or *infinite-precision real decimal arithmetic* or *exact real arithmetic*.
Example:

$$\frac{1}{3} = .33333\ldots = \sum_{n=1}^{\infty} 3 \cdot 10^{-n}$$

2. *Machine arithmetic* or *finite-precision real* (decimal or binary, rounded or unrounded, fixed-point or floating-point) *arithmetic*.
Examples:

$$\frac{1}{3} \approx .333$$

$$(1.01) \cdot (3.01) \approx .304$$

$$(2.10 \cdot 10^{-4}) \cdot (1.03 \cdot 10^{-6}) \approx 2.16 \cdot 10^{-10}$$

3. *Exact-interval arithmetic* or *infinite-precision interval arithmetic*.
Example:

$$[1, 2]/[2, 3] = [.333\ldots, 1.0]$$

$$= \left[\frac{1}{3}, 1.0\right]$$

4. *Rounded-interval arithmetic* or *finite-precision interval arithmetic*.
Examples:

$$[1, 2]/[2, 3] \subset [.333, 1.00]$$

$$\frac{1}{3} \subset [.3333, 3334]$$

$$[1.200, 1.230] + [1.060, 234.5] \subset [2.260, 235.8]$$

APPENDIX 2   FLOW CHART OF THE Kth-ORDER METHOD
FOR THE INITIAL-VALUE PROBLEM

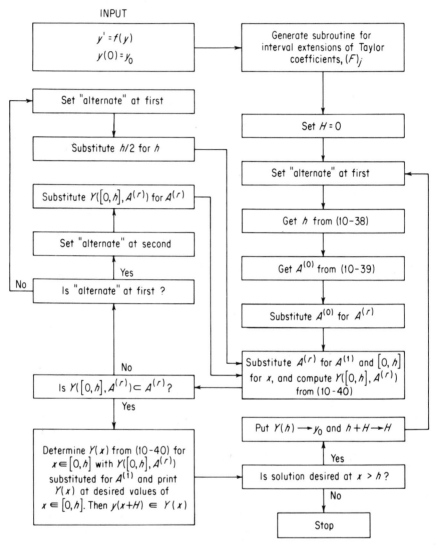

INDEX